PRINCESS IVONA
THE MARRIAGE
OPERETTA

THREE PLAYS

WITOLD GOMBROWICZ
THREE PLAYS

PRINCESS IVONA
THE MARRIAGE
OPERETTA

Introductory Essay by Jerzy Peterkiewicz

Translated by Krystyna Griffith-Jones,
Catherine Robins and Louis Iribarne

Marion Boyars
London . New York

This volume first published in 1998 in an original paperback edition by
Marion Boyars Publishers Ltd, 24 Lacy Road, London SW15 1NL

Princess Ivona:
First published in Warsaw 1938 in the quarterly magazine 'Skamander'
First published in Great Britain 1969 by Calder and Boyars Limited
© Witold Gombrowicz 1969
English translation © Krystyna Griffith-Jones 1969

Operetta:
First published in Great Britain 1971 by Calder and Boyars Limited
© Witold Gombrowicz 1969
English translation © Marion Boyars 1971

The Marriage:
First published in France 1953 in the Polish-language review 'Kultura'
First published in Great Britain 1970 by Calder and Boyars Limited
© Witold Gombrowicz 1953
© Grove Press 1969

British Library Cataloguing in Publication Data

Gombrowicz, Witold
    Three Plays: 'Princess Ivona', 'The Marriage', and 'Operetta'
    I. Title   II. Griffith-Jones, Krystyna
    III. Iribarne, Louis
    891.8527

ISBN 0–7145–2965–6

CONTENTS

Introduction   7

Princess Ivona   13

The Marriage   79

Operetta   201

ABOUT THE AUTHOR

Witold Gombrowicz was born in 1904, studied law in Warsaw, published his best novel *Ferdydurke* in 1937 and his first play *Princess Ivona* a year later. The outbreak of the War found him in Argentina where he had to live for over twenty years. In 1953 he unmasked his Polishness in a highly stylised mock-memoir, *Trans-Atlantic*, and embarked on a long and fastidious Diary, in which the first entry reads: 'Monday: me, Tuesday: me, Wednesday: me, Thursday: me.'

In 1963 he went to Berlin, then settled in the South of France where he died in 1969. Gombrowicz is better known in France and Germany than in Britain or the United States, although three of his novels and three plays are available in English. These are: *Ferdydurke*, tr. Eric Mosbacher (MacGibbon & Kee, 1961, Marion Boyars); *Pornografia*, tr. A. Hamilton (Marion Boyars, 1966); *Cosmos*, tr. Eric Mosbacher (MacGibbon & Kee, 1967); *Possessed*, tr. J.A. Underwood, 1980; *Princess Ivona*, tr. K. Griffith-Jones and C. Robins, 1969; *The Marriage*, tr. L. Iribarne, 1970; *Operetta*, 1971, Marion Boyars, who also published *A Kind of Testament*, 1973. *The Diaries* in two volumes are published by Quartet Books, 1988 and 1989.

INTRODUCTION

THE FORK AND THE FEAR
Remembering Gombrowicz
By Jerzy Peterkiewicz

Gombrowicz at a café in Warsaw, shocking literary ladies with a fork. He picked his teeth with it. The café was called *The Country-Squire's*, but the adjectival form of the name in Polish somehow obscured the image of the squire. Translated into English or French, the name becomes visual; it exudes an almost grotesque *bonhomie*. So I see Gombrowicz at his favourite table as a squire on a prolonged visit to the capital, an absentee landlord, not quite here and never there. In later years he was to be haunted by precisely this mask which many of his foreign reviewers wanted him to wear. A Pole, therefore a nobleman: such a convenient label. He grew tired of it, understandably.

In 1936, however, he acted the part as if determined to impose this social cliché not only on the snobbish hangers-on, but also on his friends. As soon as he saw it was fully accepted, he would start poking at his own image with a word, a gesture, or a fork. An idiosyncratic squire can simulate bad manners. Look, I did that, therefore it is done. A circle of literary buddies, their female companions in particular, were duly impressed.

All social shocks and counter-snobberies are infantile because their urge is regressive. Ferdydurke with his pants down, unpunishable for indecent exposure — all is part of the same game in the *kindergarten* of society.

> 'Oh, there are plenty of more or less puerile places in the world, but a country house is perhaps the most puerile of all. Here both masters and people turned themselves into children, preserved themselves by turning themselves into children, they were children to each other. Advancing barefoot along the corridor under the mask of night, I seemed to re-enter my aristocratic and pre-pubertal past . . . I succumbed to the anachronistic idea of a gigantic super-slap — an idea at one and the same time

infantile and in accordance with immemorial tradition — a gigantic super-slap which should simultaneously liberate both master and child.' (*Ferdydurke*, ch.14).

Gombrowicz acted his tricks, made himself recognizable; he exaggerated to remain memorable. But memory is also an actor who exaggerates. In my recollections of Gombrowicz I have no continuous sequence from those Warsaw years; I see him in isolated scenes, each grotesquely augmented. And the voice so nasal that it seemed to prolong words — his fine nostrils quivering, like those of a thoroughbred colt, ready to snort at any moment. Or those regressively progressive walks at night in the summer. On the way home, 'Come with me,' he would say, 'as far as Three Crosses Place' — so we walked and talked. Warsaw was not a big town, and soon there loomed the three crosses. 'Now I'll walk you half-way back,' he said. I lived near the river, and down-hill we went. Then it was my turn to be polite. Back to the Three Crosses. On good talking nights we could do that for hours, progressing and regressing through Warsaw.

Gombrowicz had rooms in a residential suburb, in a flat belonging, I think, to one of his aunts. An object on display was a pianola, and he teased his guests with mechanical tunes in much the same manner as he teased the café crowd with a fork. Look, how we love music, every Pole is a potential Chopin; so let's have Maestro Witold doing the grand stuff at the pianola.

Mock-Polishness, like the mock-squire, was a style against the style, the anti-cliché. He remained faithful to this technique and there are revealing pages in his *Diaries* where he attacks the obsession: what-do-they-think-of-us? This adulation of the West by his countrymen — we are as good as they are, our bards are just like their bards, our cafés are just like their cafés. The same tunes of an old pianola to be replayed without effort.

But Ferdydurke doesn't care about *them* and their opinion: he shows the world his Polish tongue, a juvenile jester incapable of keeping a solemn face. That's what I am, my own immaturity can teach as much history as the stuffed eagles in the patriotic zoo.

In *The Marriage*, the hero pleads:

Enough of these gods! Give me man!
May he be like me, troubled and immature,

Confused and incomplete, dark and obscure
So that I can dance with him! Play with him!
Fight with him!
Pretend to him! Ingratiate myself with him!
And rape him, love him and forge myself
Anew from him, so I can grow through him. . .

One of the best comments on Gombrowicz's involvement with his native tradition came years ago from Professor Folkierski, a comparativist of unusual acumen (he was, significantly enough, half-French). It was soon after the publication of *Trans-Atlantic* and the professor said to me: 'You know, Gombrowicz is more traditional than one would imagine, he is the literary heir of Henryk Rzewuski, he works within the style of *gaweda* (a chatty narrative), the only form we Poles treat as our own invention.' This sounded ironic: choosing an old-fashioned formula to explain a modern novelist, but Folkierski was too subtle for a mere reversal of terms. He stated something critically accurate.

Rzewuski (1791–1866), a pro-Russian aristocrat and a tireless raconteur, exploited the casual and anecdotal manner of social prattle in a collection of tales about originals, cranks and practical jokers in the Polish nobility of the 18th century. His own fictitious raconteur was a certain Soplica, a noble of course, and a candid admirer of every extravagance and absurdity which his class tolerated for the sheer joy of living, despite the approaching end of the Polish kingdom. Instinctively, Gombrowicz adopted this stylistic buffoonery because it suited him well, with its polite forms of address, its nudging asides and regressive humour. Moreover, it was the best medium with which to capture the self-perpetuating myth of adolescence, whether personal or national. Now he could laugh at the inflating preoccupation of Poles with their Polishness, which is not unlike the Frenchmen's preoccupation with their communal ethos. *La Gloire* and Self-destruction, the dichotomy of a patriotism which is particularly good at accusing. *J'accuse* of Emile Zola. Writing on the wall, putting men against the wall. Adolescents love scribbling their righteous protests on walls, and common citizens invariably fall short of the demands of the national Super-Ego. The language they inherit is also their undoing.

Gombrowicz understood his national identity because he was partly in love with *La Gloire* of his own ego. Perhaps the Pole is an *enfant terrible* among the Slavs, asking awkward questions, always on the run from the parental myth.[1] A squire or a peasant, he has enough aristo-cratic defiance to accept disillusionment.

Writers do not, on the whole, acknowledge those literary debts which have affected their style: these are probably too intimate to reveal, even if one keeps a diary for public confessions, as Gombrowicz did. His manner of writing stemmed from his Polish predecessors, both 19th century and more recent. Parody and mimicry need models to work on: a style cannot pull faces at nothing. The past was more useful to Gombrowicz than the present. And there were iconoclasts of genius before him. Irzykowski was one of them. His *Paluba*, a very early psycho-analytical novel (1903), owed nothing to Freud, but it probed deeply into patterns of self-deception, into bashful moments hiding behind big words and poses, it exposed both social and patriotic cant. The author saw his experiment as the triumphant comedy of character. Ferdydurke's comedy is in essence triumphant.

Witkiewicz's novels and plays, though uneven in dialogue, had much in common with Gombrowicz's handling of the plot, now coy, now arrogant. Both he and Gombrowicz were teasers, and literary teasers do sometimes irritate. They provoke the reader or the audience, but are surprised when the provocation works.[2]

Operetta comes towards the end of Gombrowicz's development, a stylistic résumé, full of conscious echoes and obvious borrowings. The revolutionary antics remind one of *The Undivine Comedy* (1835), a visionary and violent play written by the young romantic, Krasinski. The ridiculous songs with their obsessive repetitions belong to the evergreen musical *kitsch*, but real brutality is planted in the text like a time-bomb. As an artistic instrument the operetta is a sort of pianola, with Gombrowicz banging it until the whole pretence breaks to pieces. Another recollection intervenes. Among our contemporaries at *The Country-Squire*'s was a character out of real operettas, who danced in the male chorus. Gombrowicz had a special nasal intonation whenever he addressed him, a curious respect for the triumphant courage of

---

[1] In *The Marriage*, Henry addresses his father: 'Father is a title the same as King is. Can't you speak like an ordinary man? Must you always get dressed up in some title or other?'

[2] The fairy-tale trappings of Gombrowicz's plays belong to the Theatre of the Absurd, but the weakness of this type of drama lurks in the ritual of transformation itself, without which the absurd seems unable to function.

kitsch, and though the young man soon betrayed the glitter of the stage for the dimmed lights of literature, he had passed the test.

Undoubtedly, much of the 1930s is reflected in Gombrowicz's mimicry: the grand gestures of the silent films, the teasing eroticism of popular entertainment, the impoverished families that could still afford servants. And the intellectual mania for paradox. I was not surprised to see G.K. Chesterton mentioned alongside Joseph Conrad in Gombrowicz's article which he contributed over a year ago to the *Times Literary Supplement*.[3] But of course he could not have mentioned any other names because Chesterton and Conrad were the fashionable writers in Poland before the War, read by the young in translation. Chesterton's clowning must have impressed him at the time. My feeling is that Grombowicz disliked the avant-garde writers as much as Byron disliked the romantics. In his *Diaries* he poured scorn on Borges. At the mention of Joyce he shrugged his shoulders. Nathalie Sarraute — 'yes,' he had met her, a sniff and a pause, and that was that. I sometimes suspect that he really didn't want to read any of them. But why should he? One thing remains certain: the importance of his Polish reading, from the 17th-century diarist Pasek to Sienkiewicz whom he mocked in much the same way as he mocked the world of his aunts.

He cared about language. The letters we exchanged in the last years were mainly about the translations of his works into English. He wanted my opinion about their style before they went to press. He was worried that the translators had to use the French or German versions. I argued that the translator's knowledge of his own tongue mattered more than his ignorance of Polish. The idiosyncratic style of Gombrowicz has structural patterns which can be reproduced in another language, and on the whole he translates better than most Slavonic novelists. He is essentially the writers' writer. Will he ever become popular?

The next thirty years should determine Gombrowicz's place in European literature. How his books will read in the future is difficult to predict. They are light, not ponderous, and the charm is in their lightness. The public unfortunately confounds weight with seriousness, length with permanence. Brevity may be the soul of wit, but the immortality of that soul is another question.

Fame needs an aura of perpetual mystery. Gombrowicz took pains to project himself, and in his situation he had every right to do so. He

_____

[3] Published posthumously, *Times Literary Supplement*, 25 September 1969.

argued with his critics in the *Diaries*, denigrated the denigrators and hailed those who hailed him. But my impression is that in the final analysis Gombrowicz's *Diaries* work against him. All artists are vulnerable. But Gombrowicz was so much preparing himself for the hostile world that he tended to over-explain himself. Twice I implored him to remove the personal prefaces he had written to guide his English critics. He persisted in building up a protective watch-tower. This he had done from the very beginning. In the name of sincerity, I suppose. He believed in the importance and survival of the printed word. Sometimes he seemed to forget that words too have their built-in obsolescence. They corrupt the sincerity that pushed them out. Pop art thrives on this transience.

I am glad I met him in my green youth. His integrity, his charm, his stylised manners were of the kind that elevate memories. He observed and described the regressive appetites of man at a time when fear pushed societies towards catastrophe. He was not, however, a prophet of doom; such prophets are many and are replaceable. Instead he played with a dainty fork, picking his teeth to shock the easily-shockable. How convincing is the violence of manners? The brutal forces today are horribly simple. They would knock the teeth out for a start. And then what would be the use of the fork, symbolic or otherwise? Our existence, like our literature, is becoming shock-proof.

Encounter, March 1971

PRINCESS IVONA

Translated by Krystyna Griffith-Jones
and Catherine Robins

CHARACTERS

IVONA
KING IGNATIUS
QUEEN MARGARET
PRINCE PHILIP heir to the throne
LORD CHAMBERLAIN
ISOBEL lady in waiting to the Queen
SIMON friend of the Prince
CYPRIAN
IVONA'S AUNTS
INNOCENT a courtier
CHECKERS a servant
STATE DIGNITARIES
COURTIERS
BEGGAR
LADIES OF THE COURT

ACT ONE

*The promenade — usual seats, trees, etc. The public in their
Sunday best. Enter* KING IGNATIUS, QUEEN MARGARET, PRINCE
PHILIP, LORD CHAMBERLAIN, SIMON *and* CYPRIAN *followed by
ladies and gentlemen of the court.*

QUEEN: What a wonderful sunset!

CHAMBERLAIN: Wonderful indeed, Your Majesty.

QUEEN: Truly inspiring, is it not?

CHAMBERLAIN: Exactly so, Madam, exactly.

KING: A wonderful sunset now and a jolly hand of bridge
later. . . . What?

CHAMBERLAIN: Indeed. How perfectly Your Majesty combines
an innate sense of beauty with a natural desire for the game. (*A
BEGGAR approaches*) What do you want?

BEGGAR: Help, My Lord!

KING: My Lord Chamberlain, give him a crown. Let the people
know that we have their welfare at heart.

QUEEN: Give him two. For that wonderful sunset.

LADIES: Aah!

KING: Give him three. Let's do it in style.

COURTIERS: Aah. Aah.

BEGGAR: God bless your Majesty. May the Almighty bless your
gracious Majesty, and your gracious Majesty bless the Almighty. (*Exits, singing a beggar's song*)

KING: Right now! Let's go. It won't do to be late for dinner. We've still got to make a tour of the Gardens to mingle freely with our loyal subjects. It isn't a National Day for nothing, what? (*All get ready to go except* PRINCE PHILIP) You not coming, Philip?

PHILIP: (*picking a newspaper up off the ground*) Just a moment. . . .

KING: Aha, I see. A rendez-vous, what? I was just the same at your age! Let's leave him to it. (*Exit chuckling*)

QUEEN: (*reproachfully*) Ignatius!

The trumpets sound, the court leave except PRINCE PHILIP, SIMON *and* CYPRIAN.

CYPRIAN & SIMON: This do, what a crushing bore!

PHILIP: Wait, let me read today's horoscope. (*Reading*) 'From twelve till two' . . . this isn't it. . . . Here it is: 'between seven and nine in the evening great expansion of vitality, growth of personality, excellent if hazardous ideas. This is the time for bold plans and daring enterprise'.

CYPRIAN: What use is that to us?

PHILIP: (*continues reading*) 'also for the affairs of the heart'.

SIMON: Ah, that is different. (*Pointing to some passing girls*) And there they are.

CYPRIAN: Avanti, avanti! Duty calls.

PHILIP: What do you mean — duty?

CYPRIAN: Action, action! Gloriously, deliriously. We are young, we are men. We are young men. Let us *be* young men and give work to the clergy so that they can *be* clergy. That's what I call a proper division of labour.

SIMON: Look at that elegant and seductive siren. Look at those legs!

PHILIP: Oh no. Not again? Not the same old thing?

CYPRIAN: No? But why not? Of course, again and again. What would she think if we just let her pass?

PHILIP: No.

SIMON: What? What do you mean: 'no'?

CYPRIAN: (*with astonishment*) Doesn't it give Your Highness a glorious sense of achievement to hear sweet lips say 'yes', even if it means hearing the same old thing over and over again?

PHILIP: Of course it does, of course. . . . (*Continues reading*) 'These hours favour the success of great undertakings, they bring refinement of feelings, they can be dangerous for those of exalted ambition and acute sense of dignity. Affairs started at this time may turn out to be successful or otherwise'. At least that's true. . . . (*Enter* ISOBEL) Welcome, Madam.

CYPRIAN: This is an unexpected pleasure. . . .

SIMON: A delight. . . .

ISOBEL: Good evening, Your Highness. What are you doing here, away from the Court?

PHILIP: Exactly what I should be doing: while the presence of my Father inspires the hearts of our loyal men I am here to inspire delicious dreams in the hearts of our ladies . . . but you, shouldn't you be attending the Queen?

ISOBEL: I am late. I am rushing there now. I have been for a walk. . . .

PHILIP: You are in a rush? Where to?

ISOBEL: Your Highness seems a little distrait? Your voice sounds melancholy. Aren't you enjoying life any more, Your Highness? I am, to the full.

PHILIP: So am I. . . . That's why. . . .

CYPRIAN, SIMON, ISOBEL: What?

PHILIP: Humph. . . .

CYPRIAN, SIMON, ISOBEL: That's why what?

PHILIP: Oh, nothing.

ISOBEL: Nothing? Are you not well, Your Highness?

SIMON: A cold?

CYPRIAN: Migraine?

PHILIP: Wrong, wrong again! I am seething, I tell you, throbbing and bubbling inside.

CYPRIAN: (*staring at a girl*) Not bad, that blonde. Not at all bad.

PHILIP: Blonde? If you said brunette it would be exactly the same . . . (*Looking round, depressed*) trees and more trees, they are all exactly the same. I want something to happen.

SIMON: Look, another one.

CYPRIAN: Chaperoned!

SIMON: Two aunts!

ISOBEL: What is this game?

CYPRIAN: Look, Your Highness, look. One could die of laughter.

SIMON: Be quiet. Let's listen.

1st AUNT: Let's sit down. Can you see those young men, my child?

IVONA: (*silent*)

1st AUNT: Do smile, my child, always smile.

IVONA: (*silent*)

2nd AUNT: Why so clumsy, child? Why can't you smile properly?

IVONA: (*silent*)

2nd AUNT: Yesterday again you had no success whatsoever. No success today, no success tomorrow. Why are you so unattractive, my child? Unglamorous, unseductive. Nobody ever looks at you. You are a trial, that's what you are.

1st AUNT: We have spent all our savings to buy this dress for you. You can't blame us for not trying. . . .

CYPRIAN: The monstrous scarecrow!

ISOBEL: 'Monstrous' is going a little far.

SIMON: Look at her! She dares to look. . . .

CYPRIAN: The miserable wretch, the cry baby. Come, let's show her how despicable she is. We'll snub her, put her in her place.

SIMON: Yes, let's deflate this puffed up misery. This is our appointed duty. You first, I'll follow.

They march in front of IVONA, *bursting into laughter under her nose.*

CYPRIAN: Ha, ha, ha, right under her nose.

ISOBEL: Oh leave her alone. It's just silly.

1st AUNT: (*to* IVONA) You see what you have let us in for?

2nd AUNT: To be a public laughing stock. Oh, you are a trial. I thought that in my old age, when I ceased to be a woman, I would cease to be a butt of ridicule. Now I am old and as ridiculous as ever. Why? Just because of you.

CYPRIAN: Do you hear? The aunts are at it too. Go on! Give it to her!

2nd AUNT: They are laughing at us again. If we leave now, they will laugh behind our backs. But if we stay, they will laugh in our faces.

1st AUNT: My child, last night, at the dance, why didn't you even lift a finger?

2nd AUNT: Why will nobody take any interest in you? Do you think we like it? Such sexual ambition as we ever had we have invested in you and you do nothing; you don't even ski.

1st AUNT: Why don't you try pole vaulting? Other girls do. . . .

CYPRIAN: Oh, look at the jellyfish. She makes me squirm, sets me on edge. She annoys me more than I can say. I can't bear it. I'm going to throw them off their seat, shall I?

SIMON: No — it isn't really worth the trouble. It would do just as well to shake your finger or to wave your hand or do anything else for that matter. Whatever you do to her turns into a snub. (*Sniffs*)

2nd AUNT: Look, now they're sniffing at us.

ISOBEL: Do leave her alone.

CYPRIAN: No, don't. Let's play a real joke on her. I'll pretend I'm maimed, I have a club foot, and it will make her think that not even the lamest dog would deign to lick the crumbs thrown from her table. (*Moves towards* IVONA)

PHILIP: Stop. I have a much better idea.

CYPRIAN: I withdraw and leave the field to you.

SIMON: What's the idea? You look as if you were on to something this time.

PHILIP: More than you think. (*Approaches the* AUNTS) Will you allow me to introduce myself? I am His Highness, Prince Philip, the heir to the throne.

AUNTS: Aah!

PHILIP: Ladies, you seem to be having trouble with this young person. Why is she so apathetic?

1st AUNT: It is our misfortune. She is suffering from an organic deficiency, from sluggishness of the blood.

2nd AUNT: It makes her swell in winter and stink in summer. She has catarrh in the autumn and headaches in the spring.

PHILIP: It must make it difficult to choose the right season for anything. Is there no cure for her?

1st AUNT: The doctors say that if she were to become livelier, her blood would flow faster and then she might be cured.

PHILIP: But why doesn't she get livelier?

1st AUNT: Because her blood is too sluggish.

PHILIP: You mean if she became livelier her blood would flow faster and if her blood would flow faster she would become livelier. Most peculiar, a real vicious circle. Do you know what I think. . . .

2nd AUNT: Your Highness is laughing at us of course. You are welcome to, I am sure.

PHILIP: Laughing at you? No, I am not laughing at all. (*The clock strikes seven*) The hour is too serious. Don't you feel a certain expansion of vitality, a growth of personality, a kind of ecstasy even?

1st AUNT: I'm afraid not. A little chilly, perhaps?

PHILIP: Odd. (*To* IVONA) Don't you feel anything?

IVONA: (*silent*)

2nd AUNT: What could she possibly feel?

PHILIP: Do you know that the moment one looks at you, one is tempted to harm you in some way? To tie you up with a rope for instance and then to run at full speed or to drive you as a sort of milk cart. I would like to prick you with a pin and to make silly faces at you. You get on everybody's nerves. Don't you see you are like a red rag to a bull. You are provoking, you insense everyone, you drive people to distraction. Everyone has his personal irritant, but you are the universal irritant. The way you sit, the way you fiddle with your fingers and wiggle your toes. It's quite incredible. It's splendid in a way, a revelation of sorts. How do you manage to do it?

IVONA: (*silent*)

PHILIP: It is your silence, the way you look offended. The sublime air of a proud queen. You are disdainful, you are soured, arrogance and vinegar. I recognize that for everyone there is, somewhere, somebody capable of firing them to a white heat; you do that to me, you must be mine, you shall be mine. (SIMON *and* CYPRIAN *draw nearer*) Simon and Cyprian, let me introduce you to this offended queen, this proud Anaemia. . . . Look, her lips are moving. She would say something spiteful, if only she could think of something to say.

ISOBEL: How ridiculous. (*Draws nearer*) Do leave her alone. It isn't funny and it's becoming most distasteful.

PHILIP: (*sharply*) Did you ever think it wouldn't be?

CYPRIAN: Allow me to introduce myself: I am Count Acidity.

SIMON: Ha, ha, ha. I am Baron Leukemia. The joke is perhaps not subtle but certainly appropriate.

ISOBEL: Haven't you had enough? Leave the wretched creature alone.

PHILIP: Wretched? Not so fast, dear lady. What would you say if I told you that I were going to marry this wretched creature?

SIMON & CYPRIAN: Ha, ha, ha.

PHILIP: This is not a laughing matter. I will marry her (SIMON *and* CYPRIAN *laugh*) . . . I will marry her. I simply have to. She is my own turmoil. I will marry her. (*To the* AUNTS) I may have your permission, mayn't I?

SIMON: It is you who are going too fast and too far with this joke. It won't be funny if they sue you for breach of promise.

PHILIP: A joke? And isn't she herself a colossal joke? Can't I be a joke as well? The balance is perfect: I am a prince, she is a proud and affronted queen. Just look at her. (*To* IVONA) Madam, may I be allowed to request your hand in marriage?

1st AUNT: Good gracious.

2nd AUNT: Good gracious. Your Highness has a generous heart.

1st AUNT: Your Highness is a true philanthropist.

CYPRIAN: Incredible.

SIMON: Mad. I beg you in the name of your ancestors.

CYPRIAN: I beg you in the name of your descendants.

PHILIP: Stop, both of you. (*Takes* IVONA*'s hand*)

ISOBEL: The King.

CYPRIAN: The King.

SIMON: The King.

Trumpets, trumpets etc. Enter the KING, *the* QUEEN, *the* LORD CHAMBERLAIN, *followed by ladies and gentlemen of the court.*

AUNTS: We better make ourselves scarce before the storm breaks.

The AUNTS *flee.*

KING: Still here, what!, Philip? I see you are having fun. (*To his entourage*) Didn't I tell you? My own flesh and blood.

QUEEN: Ignatius.

KING: I told you, what! What did I say? Blood runs thicker than water, like father like son, what! (*Aside*) Good Lord, this nymph seems a little. . .? What is this frump, my son?

PHILIP: Allow me, Sir, to present my future wife.

KING: Your what?

ISOBEL: His Highness is joking, of course.

KING: Joking, now I see. Just like his father. Practical jokes are about the only thing I still enjoy these days. The funny thing is, the simpler the joke, the more it pleases me. I really don't know why. There are no jokes like the old jokes, what! The simpler they are, the younger they make me feel.

CHAMBERLAIN: Exactly so, Your Majesty. May I concur with your judgement. Nothing is more rejuvenating than a really senseless joke.

QUEEN: (*embarrassed*) Philippe. . . .

PHILIP: This is not a joke.

QUEEN: What is it then, Philippe, if it's not a joke. . . .

PHILIP: It is my betrothal.

KING: What!!!

The court flee in panic.

QUEEN: We must keep our temper at all costs. We must proceed with tact. (*To* IVONA) Would you mind looking at that tree over there. (*To* PRINCE PHILIP) Philippe you are putting her in an impossible position. You are putting us in an impossible position, you are putting yourself in an impossible position. (*To the* KING) Calmly Ignatius, calmly.

PHILIP: Your Majesties, I see that in your eyes I have done something outrageous. That I, the Prince of the blood, should be linked to a person like this. . . .

KING: Now you are talking sense.

PHILIP: I don't see it like that at all. I am not taking her because I have too little, but because I have too much. Surely this is not wrong, and I am not lowering myself.

KING: Too little? Too much? What do you mean 'too much'?

PHILIP: Am I not rich enough to take on this misery? Why, pray, should only prettiness attract me. Who says so? What is wrong with being ugly? Is there a law against it? Even if it were the law, I would not follow it blindly. I am free.

KING: You can't be serious, Philip. Pride has gone to your head. Why must you muddle quite simple things? You meet a pretty girl, you like her, you naturally . . . what? If she isn't pretty, on the other hand, you equally naturally run as fast as you can. There is nothing complicated about it, it is the law of nature. As for myself (*A cautious glance at the* QUEEN) I follow it willingly, to be sure.

PHILIP: This law of nature seems to me stupid, vulgar, ridiculous and unjust.

CHAMBERLAIN: It must be so, if you say so, Sir, but all the same the most stupid laws of nature are the most delectable, Your Highness.

KING: Are you bored, Philip? Are you weary of your studies at the faculty of advanced furnace construction? What about your splendid welfare work among our poorer subjects?

QUEEN: And all your childhood games — tennis, bridge, polo? And football and dominoes?

CHAMBERLAIN: Is it possible, if I may be allowed to put it somewhat plainly, that it is that very freedom of sexual behaviour among your contemporaries which is the cause of your ennui, Your Highness? It is a little hard to believe, I must admit. I don't think it would have bored me.

PHILIP: To hell with sexual freedom. I am going to marry, that's all.

KING: To marry. To marry, indeed. You damnable insolent puppy.

I'll teach you to laugh at us, I'll curse you . . . cast you out.

QUEEN: Ignatius, you couldn't do that.

KING: I will do it. I will lay a curse on him. I will put him in irons. I will throw him out into the street.

QUEEN: Ignatius, oh Ignatius. It would cause such a scandal. Ignatius, he is only doing it out of the goodness of his heart.

KING: Out of the goodness of his heart, indeed! He's breaking his old father's heart.

QUEEN: He is doing it out of pity. He has always been so tender and the misfortunes of this miserable girl must have moved him deeply. Oh, Ignatius, it would cause such a scandal if you did anything rash.

KING: (*suspiciously*) Her misfortune has moved him? Is that what you think?

CHAMBERLAIN: Your Majesty, the Queen is so right. His Highness is doing it entirely out of his natural generosity. It is a generous deed, a noble deed. (*Aside to the* KING) Don't you see, Sire, unless we call it a generous deed, it is a scandalous one as surely as two and two makes four. You know, Sire, how obstinate Prince Philip is. We must avoid scandal at all costs.

KING: Yes! Well, well . . . on second thoughts we have to admit that your action was well intentioned. Although very, very rash, of course, what? Generosity, that's it. Generosity, what!

PHILIP: It isn't generosity at all.

QUEEN: (*talking very fast*) But it is, it is. Philippe, dear, do not interrupt. We know best. In recognition of your goodness we will allow you to present your fiancée to us. The way she bears misfortune has appealed to our best, most refined feelings. It has indeed affected us deeply. We will receive her at the palace as one equal to the highest in the land. This, we are sure, will not bring discredit on our house, but indeed exalt it.

PHILIP: (*interrupts*) Simon, send her here — Their Majesties have consented.

QUEEN: Ignatius, calm, remember!

PHILIP: (*approaches, leading* IVONA *on his arm. The courtiers emerge from under the trees. Trumpets, trumpets, etc*) Your Majesties, may I be allowed to present my fiancée?

CHAMBERLAIN: (*in a whisper*) Curtsey. Curtsey.

IVONA: (*nothing*)

CHAMBERLAIN: Curtsey, curtsey.

PHILIP: Curtsey.

QUEEN: Here, here. . . . (*She bows slightly to give* IVONA *a hint*) Now . . . now. . . .

KING: (*bows slightly as the* QUEEN *has just done*)

IVONA: (*nothing*)

PHILIP: (*a little perplexed*) This is the King, my father, His Majesty and this is the Queen, my mother, Her Majesty. Curtsey. Curtsey.

IVONA: (*nothing*)

QUEEN: (*hurriedly*) Philippe, my dear, we are touched . . . the sweet creature . . . (*Kissing* IVONA) my child, we will be mother and father to you, we are delighted with the truly evangelical spirit of our son, we respect his choice. Philippe, no retreat! Upwards and onwards for ever.

CHAMBERLAIN: Aah!

COURTIERS: (*on a signal from* CHAMBERLAIN) Aah!

KING: (*absolutely blank*) . . . upwards . . . onwards . . . I suppose you could put it like that.

QUEEN: (*continues hurriedly*) Now take her in and order her apartments to be made ready, see that she lacks nothing.

CHAMBERLAIN: Aaa. . . .

COURTIERS: Aaa. . . .

Exit PRINCE PHILIP, IVONA, SIMON *and the courtiers.*

KING: Oh, oh, she . . . we . . . damn . . . my goodness me, do you see what happened? In the end we had to bow to her . . . she wouldn't . . . and she didn't . . . ugh. Isn't she a horror!

QUEEN: Isn't she? That is the beauty of his deed!

CHAMBERLAIN: Quite so, Your Majesty, quite so. If I may coin a phrase: the uglier the betrothed, the more beautiful the betrothal. Sire, the Prince will get over it in a few days if we don't force the issue. I will see him today to find out what his intentions are. It's just an extravaganza and we must not cross him in any way if we don't want to make things worse. We must keep our peace, watch our step and proceed with caution.

QUEEN: And tact, Ignatius, and tact.

ACT TWO

The Prince's apartments. Enter PRINCE PHILIP, SIMON, IVONA.
CHECKERS, *duster in hand, comes in through opposite door.*

PHILIP: Get out, Checkers. (CHECKERS *leaves*) Make her sit
down. I am still afraid she may run away. Should we tie her to
the table leg?

SIMON: She's half dead, she won't run, Philip.

PHILIP: Well?

SIMON: (*disapproving*) Why are you doing this, Philip?

PHILIP: Why? Why? Don't you see that she's my own dragon to
be slain, my Gordian knot to be cut. I am a hunter in the night,
going single-handed after a lion. I am Theseus taking the bull
by the horns. Simon. . . .

SIMON: One can't get any sense out of you today.

PHILIP: Or it may just be irresistable curiosity. Rather as if one
were prodding a worm with a stick to see if it will turn.

SIMON: Will you let me tell you what I think?

PHILIP: Do. . . .

SIMON: Let us leave her alone. In half an hour's time we won't
know what to do with her. It will be very inconvenient apart
from anything else. You were far too rash.

PHILIP: I thought both you and Cyprian were rash enough with
her.

SIMON: Quite true, we were. But it is one thing to have a little
joke in the open air and a different thing to drag her indoors.
My advice is to let her go at once.

PHILIP: Look at the way she sits. Incredible! All the same, what impertinence. Just because this girl is as she is, must one assume that she can't attract anyone at all? Infernal cheek on the part of nature. (*Looks at* IVONA) Do you know, it is only since I first set eyes on her that I have really felt . . . no, that I have become fully a prince. Before that I felt no more than a baron and one of the lesser ones at that.

SIMON: How very odd. I would have said the opposite is the case. Since you saw her you have behaved more like a baron than a prince.

PHILIP: It is odd but I must tell you that I have never felt so self assured, so splendid, so brilliant. Tra, la, la. . . . (*Places a pen upside down on the end of his finger*) Look, I could never do this before. Apparently it is necessary to find someone truly inferior to appreciate one's own excellence. To be a prince in name is nothing — to be a prince in essence, it's heaven, it's pure joy. I am floating on air. (*He dances round the room*) Now let us have a look at our splendid folly, our magnificent distraction. Madam, could you be prevailed upon to speak?

IVONA: (*silent*)

PHILIP: You know, it's not that she's wholly ugly; it is that element of misery within her composition.

SIMON: That is the worst of it.

PHILIP: Madam, why are you like this?

IVONA: (*silent*)

PHILIP: Silence, silence, why are you like this?

IVONA: (*silent*)

SIMON: No answer. Offended.

PHILIP: Offended.

SIMON: Perhaps not offended. Just scared.

PHILIP: A little overwhelmed?

IVONA: (*quietly and uneasily*) Please, leave me alone. I am not offended.

PHILIP: Not offended, then why don't you answer?

IVONA: (*silent*)

PHILIP: Well?

IVONA: (*silent*)

PHILIP: Can't you? Why?

IVONA: (*silent*)

SIMON: Ha. Ha. She can't. She is feeling offended after all.

PHILIP: Madam, please, be kind enough to explain to us your mechanism. You are not all that stupid. Why then do people treat you as if you could not tell black from white. Are they just teasing you?

SIMON: She isn't stupid, she's in a stupid situation.

PHILIP: You are right. I beg your forgiveness. Look, Simon, isn't it amazing? Her nose is well proportioned, and she is not brainless. In fact, she is not a bit worse than many of the girls we know. But nobody would dream of teasing others as they tease you, would they? Why are you the scapegoat? Has it become a habit?

IVONA: (*quietly*) It is a wheel, it goes round and round in circles.

SIMON: What wheel?

PHILIP: Don't interrupt. What wheel?

IVONA: It is going round and round, always, everybody, every-thing, all the time.

PHILIP: Round and round? Why round? There is something mystical about it: a wheel? All circles are mystical. For exam-ple, she is lethargic. Why? Because she is out of sorts. And why is she out of sorts? Because she is lethargic, of course. Don't you see it is a circle? A vicious circle.

SIMON: (*to* IVONA) It's your own fault, cheer up a little, you bumpkin.

IVONA: (*silent*)

PHILIP: She dismissed you like a school boy, don't you see?

SIMON: Come now, pluck up courage. A little humour. A little life. Look, you are just sulking. Smile a little and all will be well.

PHILIP: Smile just a little. It won't hurt.

IVONA: (*silent*)

PHILIP: She won't. She is quite right not to. . . . It would be so out of keeping. It would only make things worse. She would be even more annoying, more irritating, more provoking, wouldn't she? Simon, I have never seen anything like it. Isn't it magnificent? What do you think would happen if we smiled at her first?

SIMON: It wouldn't work, it would be a pitying smile. A smile of pity wouldn't really do, would it?

PHILIP: Isn't it an absolutely hellish combination, an infernal dialectic. You can see, can't you, for all that she keeps silent as the grave, she herself has thought it all out. There is a method in it, it's a system, a perpetuum mobile. Inside everything is spinning, as if a dog and a cat were tied to the same pole, the dog chasing the cat and frightening it, the cat chasing and frightening the dog, a mad chase without end. But what does one see? Nothing.

SIMON: A hermetic, self contained system.

PHILIP: It couldn't have been like this always, though, could it? Not at the beginning? Why are you afraid? Because you are shy. But why are you shy? Because you are afraid, a little. Which came first? There must have been a beginning.

IVONA: (*silent*)

PHILIP: Let me see. There must be something in you — something positive as it were, a spark? You can't consist only of deficiencies. There must be something, some reason, some quality, a mainstay of sorts. Something you like in yourself, that you believe in. I promise you, we will fan that spark into a blaze. It will make your cheeks rosy.

IVONA: (*silent*)

PHILIP: Wait. This is important. Suppose someone comes up to you and tells you that you are a horror, an abomination and a curse. Striking, wounding, killing words. What would you reply? Would you say: 'Yes, I am all this, it's true, but. . . .' But what? What would you say?

IVONA: (*silent*)

SIMON: Come, tell us.

PHILIP: But . . . for instance, 'But I am kindhearted' or 'But I am nice'. Don't you see? One positive quality, one virtue, is all we need.

SIMON: (*violently*) Do say something. Speak, madam, speak.

PHILIP: Perhaps you write poetry: elegies, epitaphs? However bad they are I would recite them with enthusiasm, I swear. Oh, couldn't you give me just something to build on? Do you, in fact, write poetry?

IVONA: (*silent*)

SIMON: She despises it.

PHILIP: Do you believe in God? Do you pray? Do you kneel? Do you believe that Christ Our Lord died on the Cross for you?

IVONA: (*contemptuously*) Yes.

PHILIP: A miracle. At last. Glory be to God. But why with such contempt? You can't speak with contempt about the God you believe in.

SIMON: It is beyond me.

PHILIP: I will tell you something, Simon. She only believes in God because of her deficiencies. She knows that if she were like other people, she would not believe. She believes in God but she knows all the time that God is only a sort of dressing to cover up her psychosomatic sores. (*To* IVONA) Isn't it so?

IVONA: (*silent*)

PHILIP: Brr . . . even so, there is some appalling lethargic wisdom in it.

SIMON: Medicine. Medicine. Pills and a suitable treatment would cure that wisdom of hers. General hygiene — a morning walk — sports and games — rolls and butter.

PHILIP: You forget her body does not assimilate medicine. It does not do so because it is too sluggish. We know that sequence. It doesn't assimilate remedies for sluggishness because it is too sluggish. You are forgetting the mystic cycle. The morning walks and games would of course cure her weakness but she can't go for walks because she is too weak. Simon, have you ever heard anything like it? It calls for pity, but what a curious kind of pity. . . .

SIMON: (*to* IVONA) It must be a punishment for your sins. You must have misbehaved prodigiously in your childhood. Philip, there must be sin at the bottom of this. It could not have happened without a monumental lapse. You have sinned.

IVONA: (*silent*)

PHILIP: Oh, at last, I have grasped it, at last. Listen, if you are so weak, then you must feel everything less strongly, suffer less, less and less. Do you hear? The circle closes to your advantage, it all evens out. You know less of the fascination of the world, but it must also hurt you less.

IVONA: (*silent*)

PHILIP: Well?

IVONA: (*silent, gives a furtive glance at* PRINCE PHILIP)

SIMON: (*noticing*) What is she doing?

PHILIP: What?

SIMON: Nothing, really. Philip. . . .

PHILIP: (*getting anxious*) What is she doing?

SIMON: Philip. She is making eyes at you.

PHILIP: She couldn't. . . .

SIMON: Look. She is . . . positively . . . she is eating you up with her eyes. Passionately, damn it. She is squirming her way towards you. Take care. This weakness is lusting, seething with desire.

PHILIP: She's shameless, it is a scandal and a disgrace. How dare you fasten upon me? You worm, you maggot. Shall we roast her a little? Make a poker red-hot and make her dance?

SIMON: Philip, stop it.

PHILIP: There is something unbearable about her. I can't stand it. It's offensive. You are offending me. I do not wish to know about your troubles. You . . . pessimist, you . . . realist.

SIMON: Philip.

PHILIP: Look how she is sitting. . . .

SIMON: Make her get up.

PHILIP: Then she will be standing, and that will be even worse. Look at her — begging, begging for something . . . asking me. . . . Simon, we must get rid of this creature. Give me a knife. I will cut her throat with pleasure.

SIMON: For God's sake!

PHILIP: I'm joking, of course. But she is scared. She is really scared — it's foul. Why are you frightened, Madam, when it was only a joke? It was a joke — why are you taking it seriously?

SIMON: Now you are overdoing it.

PHILIP: What? I suppose so. How funny, you really think I'm overacting. Very likely. But it's her fault, not mine. It is she and not I. . . .

A bell. Enter CHECKERS.

SIMON: Who is that? (*Looks through the window*) Visitors, I think. The Lord Chamberlain and some ladies.

CHECKERS: Should I open the door?

PHILIP: They've come to pry. Let us go and tidy ourselves.

PRINCE PHILIP, SIMON *and* IVONA *leave the room.* CHECKERS *opens the door. Enter the* LORD CHAMBERLAIN, TWO GENTLE-MEN, FOUR LADIES *and* INNOCENT.

1st LADY: Nobody in? (*Looks around*)

2nd LADY: Oh, really, I can't. (*Giggles*)

1st GENTLEMAN: And what if it is serious?

CHAMBERLAIN: Quiet, please, ladies. I beg you, no giggling. (LADIES *giggle*) No giggling, I said. We must behave as if nothing has happened, if we are to find out how the wind is blowing.

1st LADY: And what if it is serious? Oh, what an idea. Look, her hat. What a hat! I can't! I have got a stitch.

2nd LADY: I am bursting!

CHAMBERLAIN: A little self control, I beg of you.

ALL GUESTS: But we can't. Stop or I will burst. Stop it. We are bursting. We are dying.

They are all laughing except INNOCENT. *Enter* PRINCE PHILIP, SIMON *and* IVONA.

ALL GUESTS: Your Highness. (*Bows and curtseys*)

CHAMBERLAIN: We were just passing. We couldn't refrain from calling. . . (*Rubs his hands*) all of us. . . .

PHILIP: Ivona, darling — I am delighted to be able to present you to my future wife.

GUESTS: Aah (*Bowing*). . . . Congratulations, congratulations.

PHILIP: My dear, overcome your shyness and say something. These ladies and gentlemen belong to the best society. Don't be afraid of them as if they were cannibals or chimpanzees from

Borneo. I apologize for my fiancée. She is exceptionally sensitive, proud and shy — somewhat difficult to get on with. (*To* IVONA) Do sit down, we can't be kept standing for ever.

IVONA: (*as if to sit on the floor*)

SIMON: Oh, no, not there.

GUESTS: Ha, ha, ha, ha.

1st GENTLEMAN: Could have sworn there was a chair there.

1st LADY: There was, but it must have run away.

GUESTS: Ha, ha, ha. Magic. A bad omen.

CHAMBERLAIN: Please, sit down. (*Moves a chair nearer*) Be careful, though.

SIMON: Hold it, so it doesn't run away again.

CHAMBERLAIN: Be kind enough to aim with care.

PHILIP: Aim well, my dear. (IVONA *sits down*) Well done.

All take seats except PRINCE PHILIP.

1st LADY: (*in an aside to* PRINCE PHILIP, *with a certain degree of familiarity*) Really, Your Highness. It's too much. I will die of laughter.

2nd LADY: (*in an aside to* PRINCE PHILIP) I will burst. I will die. It is of course the most fashionable kind of practical joke. I didn't know Your Highness had such a flair for it. Only look at her!

PHILIP: (*encouraging his guests*) Ha, ha, ha.

GUESTS: Ha, ha, ha.

PHILIP: (*louder*) Ha, ha, ha.

GUESTS: (*louder*) Ha, ha, ha.

PHILIP: (*louder*) Ha, ha, ha.

GUESTS: (*not quite sure*) Ha, ha, ha, ha. (*Laughter dies out. Silence*)

CHAMBERLAIN: (*coughs*)

1st LADY: I must leave, I'm afraid. I have just remembered an appointment. Your Highness will excuse me. . . .

2nd LADY: I have to go as well. Your Highness will forgive me, I have got an appointment too. (*In a low voice to* PRINCE PHILIP) I understand now. You have arranged it all to show us up. What a joke! Your Highness gets engaged to this simpleton to make fools of us. Your Highness must have found out about Lady Joanna's face lifts and wigs. That's why you got engaged to this peasant . . . to show her up. I can assure you that the irony of your strategem has not at least escaped me. I take my leave.

PHILIP: The irony?

1st LADY: (*who heard most of it — to* 2nd LADY) If it were intended to show up anybody it would be more likely you with your false teeth we all know of. (*To* PRINCE PHILIP) Your Highness, do not be too cruel, I beg you! And now I really must be going.

2nd LADY: My teeth. More likely your false bust.

1st LADY: What about your crooked shoulder?

2nd LADY: Remember your toes.

GUESTS: We really must be going.

PHILIP: Don't go yet.

GUESTS: It is time, Your Highness. It's time for us to go.

   The GUESTS *leave except the* LORD CHAMBERLAIN *and* INNO-CENT. *One can hear from the stairs outside:* 'toes', 'teeth', 'wig', *etc.*

CHAMBERLAIN: Forgive me, Your Highness, but I am forced to request an immediate interview with you, Sir. Your Highness has frightened our fair ladies away.

PHILIP: I did not, their own secrets have driven them away. It appears that there is nothing more frightening. Famine and war are nothing compared to one little well hidden false tooth.

INNOCENT: Excuse me.

PHILIP: What is this? You are still here?

INNOCENT: I am. I am sorry. I only wanted to say that this is vile.

PHILIP: What is vile?

INNOCENT: Vile and mean. I am sorry. I must sit down. Excitement always upsets my breathing.

PHILIP: You said something was vile?

INNOCENT: I am sorry . . . I got carried away. Forgive me, Your Highness. Forget about it, please. I am sorry. (*Wants to leave*)

PHILIP: Wait. You said something was mean and vile. Wait a moment.

INNOCENT: (*his speech alternates between deadly quiet and high irritation*) But I see now that I can't keep it up.

CHAMBERLAIN: What a silly expression. Keep up — what?

INNOCENT: Keep up what I have started. (*Wanting to leave*) I apologize.

PHILIP: Wait a moment, don't be so mysterious, Mister . . . Mr . . . Mr. . . .

INNOCENT: I love her and that is why I got carried away and started protesting. But I withdraw my protest and I beg you to forget the whole incident.

PHILIP: You? You love her?

SIMON: Well, I'll be damned!

CHAMBERLAIN: How comic.

PHILIP: You pierce my heart. This is serious. Do you know the sudden transition from frivolity to seriousness. There is holiness in it. It's a revelation.

INNOCENT: Your Highness, I am a humble man.

PHILIP: Forgive me, Ivona. Thank God, somebody can love even you. So it is possible. You have got somebody who . . . What a relief. I have done what I have because I couldn't bear you, I couldn't bear the thought of you. Forgive me, I give you my blessing. Go now. Leave me alone.

SIMON: (*looking at* IVONA, *who is bowing her head*) Crying!

PHILIP: Crying? It's happiness.

SIMON: I wouldn't trust the cry baby. Her sort only cry from unhappiness. Do you love him?

IVONA: (*silent*)

PHILIP: It doesn't matter. (*To* IVONA) Things are not so bad, now that there is somebody who loves you. (*To* INNOCENT) You are a brave person, a real man. Go on loving her. It's splendid. You have redeemed us all, we are all indebted to you.

INNOCENT: Vanity prompts me to explain that she loves me too. She doesn't like to admit it in front of the Prince, naturally, as I don't gratify her pride. (*To* IVONA) It isn't worth pretending, you have after all told me many times that you loved me.

IVONA: (*silent*)

INNOCENT: (*irritated*) Oh, don't be so uppish. If you wish to know, you attract me as little as I do you, or even less. . . .

PHILIP: What?

INNOCENT: (*calmly*) Allow me to explain, Your Highness. When I said I loved her, I meant that I loved her for want of something better, because of the absence, let us say, of. . . .

CHAMBERLAIN: Fi donc. You mustn't speak like this.

INNOCENT: The point is that desirable women or even average women are so difficult and unbending. With her one can relax. There is no competition and no showing off. I relax with her and she with me. We love one another because she is as unattractive to me as I am to her, we are equal.

PHILIP: I admire your frankness.

INNOCENT: I would lie willingly but it would be useless. Everybody sees through everything these days. The fig leaves have withered. There is nothing left but to be honest. I am not denying that our love is a consolation prize. I have as much success with women as she with men. All the same I am jealous. I have a right to show it. (*To* IVONA *with surprising passion*) You have fallen in love, haven't you? With him? Him?

IVONA: (*cries out*) Get out, go!

INNOCENT: She is in love.

IVONA: (*collapsing after her great effort*) Go. . . .

PHILIP: She spoke. But in that case . . . she spoke. You heard. That means she really loves me.

INNOCENT: It's obvious. I have lost as usual. I shall go. I am going. (*Exits*)

PHILIP: She loves me. Instead of hating me. I am cruel to her. I humiliate her. She falls in love with me and now she loves me. Because I can't stand her, she loves me. This is serious. (*Enter* CHECKERS) Go away, Checkers. What should I do?

CHAMBERLAIN: If Your Highness could be a little more lighthearted about it.

PHILIP: It can't be. . . . Tell me you don't. . . . You don't love me?

IVONA: (*silent*)

PHILIP: She loves me. I am loved by her. I am loved by her. I am her beloved . . . I am involved in her. . . She has enmeshed me. I can't look down on her if she loves me. I cannot scorn from outside because I am part of her. All this time I thought that I existed on my own, by myself — and (*Snaps his fingers*) she has caught me. She is the trap and I am captured. You love me, I must love you, I will love you. . .

SIMON: What are you going to do?

PHILIP: To start loving her!

SIMON: You can't do the impossible.

PHILIP: (*to* IVONA) Ivona, put your hat on.

SIMON & CHAMBERLAIN: Where are you going?

PHILIP: For a walk. Just the two of us. To learn to love.

   PRINCE PHILIP *and* IVONA *leave.*

SIMON: What now?

CHAMBERLAIN: She has turned his head.

SIMON: How could she? This monstrosity.

CHAMBERLAIN: Sometimes, you know, ugly women turn heads more effectively than pretty ones.

SIMON: The mind boggles.

CHAMBERLAIN: I can tell you, there is nothing more dangerous than an ugly woman. It is generally assumed that agreeable women are dangerous, but a really unpleasant woman — or, for a woman, a really unpleasant man. . . Ho, ho, ho. Truly un-appetizing women, specially when young and when the disagreeableness is of proper — ah — intensity. . . Ho, ho, ho . . . the inexperienced young man who approaches that sort of woman with undue confidence, ho, ho, ho, may get involved in really monstrous capers.

SIMON: Monstrous capers?

CHAMBERLAIN: Young man, you don't know anything about it and even I with all my experience of life don't. There are things a gentleman must know nothing about, because he would cease to be a gentleman if he did. (*Bell*) What is this?

Enter CHECKERS.

CHECKERS: Shall I admit 'em?

Enter the KING *and the* QUEEN.

QUEEN: Where is Philippe? Are they out?

CHAMBERLAIN: They have just left.

KING: We have both come to see what hot water he has got into this time. The Queen's ladies came to her shouting and scream-ing, complaining that our son had got himself engaged to that frump for a joke, just to spite them, to show up some beauty secrets, uhm . . . slight imperfections of theirs, what? If that's all he's after there's not much harm in it.

QUEEN: All the same, we can't allow it. My ladies are all terribly agitated. . . . This joke has really gone too far.

CHAMBERLAIN: If it were only a joke! We must take all possible precautions Your Majesty.

KING: Why?

CHAMBERLAIN: He is in love with her. He loves her. I can't explain it. I can't put it into words. I can't say it. It is something . . . explosive, we must all take cover or it will blow up in our faces.

KING & QUEEN: Oh, what shall we do?

ACT THREE

A room in the castle. SIMON *seated, two ladies of the Court walk through giggling, followed by* PRINCE PHILIP.

PHILIP: What are you doing?

SIMON: Sitting.

PHILIP: And what else?

SIMON: Nothing.

PHILIP: What were they talking and laughing about, the two bubbling blunderers? What were they saying?

SIMON: They were giggling. Women often do. It's their nature and it suits them best.

PHILIP: Were they laughing at me?

SIMON: Why should they? They were just laughing at each other.

PHILIP: If not at me, then at her . . . my fiancée. But surely their laughter has changed? I may be wrong but it seems to me that they in fact no longer laugh at her but at me. Everyone is whispering and giggling. Is it a delusion? Do something for me. Try to find out what they are saying about us, what kind of ridicule they are building up? I would like to know. It does not matter, of course, but I would like to know. You also might tell them that if they continue to take liberties behind my back. . . .

SIMON: What is happening to you, Philip? You are as touchy and as easily hurt as if you were your fiancée.

PHILIP: Don't go too far. I have had enough. I am not used to being a laughing stock or to having my actions and my feelings ridiculed. Tell that mob that if anyone permits himself the least impropriety, the shadow of a slight. . . .

The doors open, trumpets etc. Enter the KING, *the* QUEEN,
IVONA *and the* LORD CHAMBERLAIN, ISOBEL *and the*
COURTIERS.

QUEEN: (*to* IVONA) You liked it? You liked it, didn't you? Have
you had enough? Sufficient? (*Smiles and kisses* IVONA *ingrati-
atingly*) Perhaps another pear in syrup? A nice sweet one?

IVONA: (*silent*)

QUEEN: It would do you good. So much good.

KING: Good, good!

QUEEN: Perhaps a little cream? Cream does you good. It's so
nutritious. What about some cream? Or milk? Milk with sugar?
Lait sucre? (*Silence*) What is it? No appetite? Naughty,
naughty. What are we going to do about it?

IVONA: (*silent*)

CHAMBERLAIN: Nothing? (*Laughs benevolently*) Nothing?

KING: Nothing? (*Laughs at first benevolently, then nervously*)
Nothing? (*To* LORD CHAMBERLAIN) Nothing?

QUEEN: Nothing?

CHAMBERLAIN: Nothing at all, Your Majesty. In fact, if the truth
be told, nothing. (*Silence*)

QUEEN: Such a shy creature. So nice, so quiet. If only she would
say something occasionally. (*To* IVONA) If you would say
something sometimes, my pet. It is not difficult, really. One has
to say something sometimes — for decency's sake. It's elemen-
tary decency. You don't want to be indecent? What are we
going to do now? How will we occupy ourselves?

KING: Well?

CHAMBERLAIN: Well?

IVONA: (*silent*)

KING: What? Nothing. Surely it is impossible never to know the
answer? You can't mope around the house all day, what? — and

nothing, nothing, nil. It's such a bore, don't you see? What? (*He stares at them all in stupefaction*) Say something, for goodness' sake.

CHAMBERLAIN: Heaven help us.

QUEEN: May the Lord have mercy upon us.

Enter CHECKERS.

CHECKERS: Your Highness, the doctor has arrived and is waiting in the gallery.

PHILIP: (*to* IVONA) It is for you. Come. You will excuse us.

PHILIP *and* IVONA *leave.*

QUEEN: Philippe, just a moment . . . Philippe.

PHILIP *returns.*

QUEEN: (*to the* COURTIERS) Will you leave us, please, we have to speak to our son. (*The* COURTIERS *leave*) Philippe, you can't complain that we do not respect your feelings. We are like a mother and father to this poor child. But couldn't you use your influence to make her slightly more communicative? She hasn't said a word during tea, she hasn't said a word during lunch or breakfast for that matter. In fact she has not said a word all day long. Just think what they all think of her, and of us. The decencies should be preserved, Philippe.

PHILIP: (*sarcastically*) Decencies?

QUEEN: My dear son, aren't we offering her a mother's heart? We love her, with all her faults, because she loves you.

PHILIP: (*threateningly*) You love her? Love. See to it that you do. (*He leaves*)

QUEEN: Oh Lord, give us wisdom. Oh Lord, guide us. Ignatius, you are not showing her enough warmth, she is frightened of you.

KING: Frightened be damned. Then how does she manage to get into every corner and to look through every window? She will use up all our windows in no time at all. And still not a word, nothing at all. Frightened, my foot. (*To* LORD CHAMBERLAIN) Give me the reports. Ah, France is rising again. (*To himself*) Frightened, but of what? Of me? (*To the* QUEEN) And you are fussing around her too much. (*Imitates the* QUEEN) 'Another pear?' 'Or another little cake?' As if you were a boarding house landlady.

QUEEN: You are not fussing, you are quite natural with her aren't you? You only have to swallow every time you are about to speak to her, and you look scared whenever you are near her. Do you think that nobody has noticed?

KING: Scared? It's she who is scared. (*Murmurs*) The viper.

CHAMBERLAIN: The majesty of Your Majesty seems to intimidate her. I am not the least surprised — I too have been intimidated myself on occasions. In fact, I have trembled in the sight of Your Majesty, but may I be allowed to suggest that Your Majesty might encourage her a little: take her aside and have a little chat.

KING: With her? Me? With our Grumpy Dumpy? What. . . .

QUEEN: A splendid idea. She needs encouragement. We must arrange little talks in private, a deux or a trois. When she gets used to us we will attempt it with the others. It will stop her being so terrified. Ignatius, don't be churlish. We will start at once. I am going to send her to you under some pretext. Philip is with the doctor. I know, I will send her back for some wool. But I beg you, promise to behave like a true father to her. (*Leaves*)

KING: Lord Chamberlain, look what you've got me into. What can I talk about?

CHAMBERLAIN: Your Majesty, it is the simplest thing. You approach her, you smile to her, you say something, you tell a joke — then she, of course, will have to smile, perhaps even to laugh — then you will smile back, and so on and so forth: you will start what it might be permissible to call happy social intercourse.

KING: Smile, smile. Why should I put myself out? Because she is too shy? What? Lord Chamberlain, you do it. (*Wants to leave*)

CHAMBERLAIN: But, Sire, surely it isn't the first time you will have to put a girl at ease?

KING: It's all very well but this wretch is so scared.

CHAMBERLAIN: Everybody is afraid a little.

KING: But she is so lackadaisical about it — no guts even about being afraid, what? So dull. Oh, here she is. Wait, now, I am not going to make a fool of myself all by myself. Don't go, stay. (*The* KING *assumes a pleasant face. Enter* IVONA) Nice to see you here . . . what? (IVONA *approaches, looks round. The* KING, *good-naturedly*) Looking for something, eh?

IVONA: Wool. . . .

KING: Wool?

IVONA: Wool. . . .

KING: Oh, here it is. (*Laughs*)

IVONA *takes the wool.*

KING: Ha, ha, ha.

IVONA: (*silent*)

KING: Was it lost?

IVONA: (*silent*)

KING: Hm, hm. (*Walks up to* IVONA) What is it? What? (*Laughs*) Well, we are a little scared? There is nothing to be scared of. Nothing at all. What? (*Impatiently*) I said there's nothing to be afraid of.

IVONA: (*withdraws a little*)

KING: I am father. I am Philip's father, daddy. . . . Ugh. Not daddy, father. Anyhow, I am not a stranger. (*He comes nearer.* IVONA *withdraws further*) You mustn't . . . I am a plain, ordinary man. Well, not ordinary — but I am not an ogre. I am not a bogey man. I have not eaten any little children. There is nothing to be afraid of. I am not a beast. I am saying I am not a beast. I am not a beast. (*Nervously*) There is nothing to be afraid of. I am not a beast. (*Comes nearer still.* IVONA *backs violently, drops her wool. The* KING *shouts*) I say there is nothing to be afraid of, I am not a beast!!!

CHAMBERLAIN: No, no, tss . . . no.

KING: You snake! (IVONA *backs out of the room*)

CHAMBERLAIN: Hush. Somebody may hear you.

KING: She is scared. Scared. Scared, my foot . . . not properly scared, just indulging herself. Mammn, boo, boo, gugga.

CHAMBERLAIN: I would venture to suggest that she is not even capable of being properly afraid. Some of our ladies can be afraid beautifully, with such charm, such piquancy. This one only just manages to be scared. There is nothing to it. (*With distaste*) No frills, the plainest possible thing.

KING: I've just remembered something. . . .

CHAMBERLAIN: Remembered? What?

KING: Afraid, afraid. Lord Chamberlain, do you remember that one . . . the one we . . . a long time ago. How one forgets, what?

CHAMBERLAIN: Whom, Your Majesty?

KING: It's a long time, I have forgotten all about it till now. I was only a prince and you were only an embryo of a chamberlain. That little one we. . . . You know. . . . I think on this sofa. I think she was a seamstress.

CHAMBERLAIN: The little seamstress. The sofa. Youth, oh blissful days of youth. (*Enter* CHECKERS) What is it, Checkers? Do not interrupt. (CHECKERS *leaves*)

KING: She died soon after that, I think . . . drowned herself.

CHAMBERLAIN: She did. I remember as if it were yesterday, she walked on to a bridge and then from the bridge . . . splash . . . oh, youth, youth. There is nothing to equal it.

KING: Wouldn't you think she was rather like this Grumpy Dumpy?

CHAMBERLAIN: But, Your Majesty, this one is a bloated blonde and the other was a thin brunette.

KING: But she was scared in the same way. Bungle, botch — mamma, gugga . . . just the same. She was scared stiff, the trollop.

CHAMBERLAIN: If these memories displease Your Majesty, it is better to forget. It's better not to remember dead women. A dead woman isn't a woman at all.

KING: She was scared and she looked ill-used — just as this one. On this sofa. Ugh, why should something always remind one of something else? I can now remember the whole damn thing.

Enter the QUEEN.

QUEEN: Congratulations. Wonderful. You have put her at her ease, you have reassured her! Paralysed with fear, poor thing. What has got into you, Ignatius? You have spoilt everything.

KING: Hell and damnation, don't you come near me, Madam.

QUEEN: What's all this? Why shouldn't I come nearer?

KING: Why? Why? Always why. Can't I have any wishes of my own? Am I not my own master, what? Must I explain everything? Why are you looking at me? Why are you staring? Well? Why? Why did I rage at her? Because she reminded me of something.

CHAMBERLAIN: Not worth mentioning, Your Majesty. It isn't worth telling. . . .

KING: She reminded me about something . . . but, about *you* if you want to know, yes, about you, my darling.

QUEEN: About me?

KING: Ha, ha, ha. There is no need to stare. Hang it all, I am sorry. Margaret, I admit that I got carried away, but can you imagine, I can't even look at this poor child without thinking of you. What? I didn't want to speak about it, it is embarrasing, but if you want me to be frank, I will. You know how sometimes one person reminds us of another . . . not altogether, in sort of a different condition as it were, you understand? When I see Grumpy Dumpy . . . the way she moves . . . sloppy, groping, fumbling . . . it makes me think of you (*Whispers*) all floppy . . . and undone. . . .

QUEEN: She reminds you of me . . . undone?

KING: Exactly. Exactly what you are thinking. Say it. Say it yourself and you will see that it is the same. Whisper it to me.

QUEEN: Ignatius, my God.

KING: I see, Madam, you would rather keep your little secrets.

QUEEN: You are forgetting yourself.

KING: On the contrary, I am remembering. I am remembering all sorts of things. In a moment I shall remember all. (*Muttering*) Mamma, gugga. (*Leaves hurriedly*)

QUEEN: What does it all mean?

LORD CHAMBERLAIN *runs after the* KING. *The* QUEEN *remains, thoughtful. Enter* ISOBEL, *titivates herself in front of a looking glass.*

QUEEN: Stop titivating yourself.

ISOBEL: (*ashamed*) Your Majesty. . . .

QUEEN: You are doing it all the time. Since this . . . this . . . unfortunate creature appeared at court, you are all fidgeting, and preening yourselves. Come here now, girl, I must ask you something.

ISOBEL: Your Majesty.

QUEEN: Look at me. Look straight into my eyes. Admit it. You have told somebody. You have been prattling about my poems. Admit it. You couldn't keep the secret any longer and you told them.

ISOBEL: Your Majesty.

QUEEN: You haven't? If you have told nobody, how could he have found out? He must have found my notebook under the mattress.

ISOBEL: Who, Your Majesty?

QUEEN: That is it. That is what he meant. Look, tell me frankly
as if I weren't the Queen. I am releasing you temporarily, of
course, from all the deference due to me. Tell me the truth.
When you look at Ivona, does anyone else come to mind? No
association? The way she walks, for instance. Her nose? The
way she looks, her general behaviour? Do they remind you of
somebody? Some affinity? Do you think that a malicious
person could see some link between her and . . . and . . . and
my own . . . my poetry? My own intimate feelings I put in it.

ISOBEL: Your poetry? Your Majesty, how. . . . What is this?

QUEEN: The disastrous, the cursed poetry. The world is far too
vulgar. Disastrous ecstasies, fatal reveries, pernicious confi-
dences. You are not telling the truth. Why did he say 'floppy'?
If he had not read it, he would not use the word. Are my
rhymes so naked, so undone? 'Undone' — oh, horrible word.
But you are not telling the truth. Swear, swear by the light of
these candles. This is of the utmost gravity. Swear properly,
kneel down and take an oath. Repeat after me: I swear. . . .

Enter PRINCE PHILIP, followed by the KING *and the* LORD
CHAMBERLAIN.

PHILIP: Mother, I would like to talk to you. But I am sorry. . . .
What am I interrupting? A sorcery session?

QUEEN: No, no, she is just doing up my shoes. These shoes are
too large.

PHILIP: Why, pray, did the King frighten my fiancée?

QUEEN: Not this tone, Philippe.

PHILIP: What tone would you find suitable? What tone should I
adopt when my father bullies my fiancée for no reason and
treats her brutally? She is now half paralysed with fear. I can't
leave you with her for one moment without you maltreating her
in any way you think fit. In the circumstances I think I am
fantastically calm. (*Enter* CHECKERS) Go out, Checkers.
Mother, I would like to talk to you alone.

QUEEN: I will agree to talk to you alone if you tell me first what you are going to say. (ISOBEL *retires*)

PHILIP: I see you are being cautious, Mother. Forgive me if I say something which sounds odd. I don't know how to put it. Is it true that she reminds the King of some past sin of yours?

QUEEN: Who told you that?

PHILIP: Father. He told me that he had given her a scolding because she reminded him of your secret vice.

Enter the KING *and the* LORD CHAMBERLAIN.

QUEEN: Ignatius, what have you been telling Philippe?

KING: Nothing, except the truth, of course. He pestered me, so I told him. Why? When? What? I told him the truth. I would much rather he had pestered you than me.

QUEEN: Ignatius.

PHILIP: If only you would pay some regard to my situation: out of the blue my father assaults my fiancée. When I ask him, as I surely have a right to, why he has done it, you both start talking in riddles. How is it? Because of my mother's past sins, should my father let fly at my fiancée?

KING: Yes, I assaulted, I attacked, I let fly. And why, do you think, I did it? Is it because of my own little sins? Why are you staring, Margaret? If you stare at me, I will stare at you.

PHILIP: My parents stare at one another because of my fiancée? My mother stares at my father, my father stares at my mother, all because of my fiancée?

KING: Don't laugh at your father, Philip. And pipe down.

QUEEN: Your father was vexed and annoyed and told you the first thing that came into his mind. To stop you pestering him. It is absurd, not worth talking about. Let us change the subject.

PHILIP: Madam, I know it is absurd.

QUEEN: Let us not talk about it any more. Absolute nonsense.

PHILIP: Nonsense indeed, quite absurd, idiotic. (*Bows*)

QUEEN: Why are you bowing?

PHILIP: (*confidentially*) Because where she is concerned I am a little absurd too.

QUEEN: You, absurd?

PHILIP: It is difficult to call it anything else. I do not love her, and this makes me behave like a fool. I can see why you behave stupidly towards her, because I do the same myself.

KING: Philip, you're taking liberties. Hold your tongue. (PHILIP *bows*) Why are you bowing again, you fool? This is going too far.

PHILIP: (*confidentially*) But with her one can go as far as one likes.

KING: What? What is this? As far as one likes? I wouldn't like to go anywhere with her. What is it all about? Lord Chamberlain. . . .

QUEEN: Philippe, stop this bowing! Why are you doing it?

KING: Oh! That filthy nuisance. (*Aside*)

CHAMBERLAIN: One may be able to do anything one likes to her but that does not mean that the Prince can do anything he likes to us, does it? (*The* PRINCE *bows now to the* LORD CHAMBERLAIN *who backs in a panic*) Not to me. I had nothing to do with it. Don't come near me.

PHILIP: (*Confidentially*) Anyone can come near her, of course. One can pull her hair, one can tweak her ear.

KING: Ha, ha, ha. (*Embarrassed, stops abruptly*) I mean . . . you know . . . what?

CHAMBERLAIN: Your Highness, if you touch me, I. . . .

PHILIP: Anyone can touch her. Believe me, you can do absolutely anything you like with her. She is made for it — for anything. She is too shy to protest, too disagreeable. One can do anything. One can be stupid, idiotic, cynical, horrid. (*Bows to* LORD CHAMBERLAIN) Anything you fancy, Your Excellence.

CHAMBERLAIN: (*recoils*) I am not interested. It is a matter of complete indifference to me. (*Bows to* PRINCE PHILIP) I take my leave. (*Exit*)

KING: Rot and rubbish. Why are you staring, Philip? Good day. (*Bows*) Good day. Get out. (*Exit*)

QUEEN: What do you mean? Explain, explain. Goodbye. (*Exits*)

PHILIP: (*shouts after* LORD CHAMBERLAIN, KING *and* QUEEN) You can do anything. Everything. Whatever you like. (*To himself*) She is still sitting somewhere, by the fire, and she loves me. Loves me. . . . Whatever you like, whatever you can think of. Everything. (*Notices* ISOBEL *who has got up from a chair she has been sitting on during the preceding scene.* PRINCE PHILIP *comes up to her and kisses her neck*) You can let yourself go with her, anything goes!

ISOBEL: Let me go.

PHILIP: Oh, with her one can do just as one pleases. (*Kisses her on the lips*) Ah, delightful.

ISOBEL: (*struggling*) I will scream.

PHILIP: But I am telling you, you can do as you like with her. I am sorry, I did not mean you, didn't want to, really. It just happened . . . I am sorry. What have I done? I have behaved like a fool again.

ISOBEL: The impertinence.

PHILIP: I beg you not to tell anyone. If my fiancée were to hear of it she would be hurt. Hurt, hurt, hurt, hurt.

ISOBEL: But let me go, Your Highness.

PHILIP: (*still holding her*) In a moment . . . hurt. (*Kisses her*) What a nose, what a lovely mouth you have. Don't go. I believe I am being unfaithful. It's terrible. . . . It's glorious. It's so easy. Checkers! Checkers!

ISOBEL: (*struggling*) At least don't call anyone.

PHILIP: On the contrary my love. (*Enter* CHECKERS) Checkers, ask Master Simon to come with Miss Ivona at once. (CHECKERS *leaves*) There is no question of my letting you go. I feel at ease at last. The delight of embracing a girl who is not repulsive. I shall send you flowers. Oh, how easy it all is. I have my touch again. I must turn it to good account. I love you. (*Enter* SIMON *and* IVONA) Simon, this is my present fiancée.

SIMON: What?

PHILIP: Ivona, I must confess something to you. Just a moment ago I was unfaithful to you with Isobel. You are no longer my fiancée. I am sorry but there is nothing I can do about it. You are not desirable and Isobel is, extremely. Do not be offended that I announce it so lightly, everything will be easy from now on, (*To* ISOBEL) thanks to you, my treasure, my darling, and I intend to make use of that. (*Kisses* ISOBEL'*s hand. To* IVONA) Why are you standing like this? Actually you can stand as you like, it doesn't matter any more. Farewell. I am going, moving away, further and further away from you. I am breaking it off. I warn you, you won't gain anything by standing there.

SIMON: She won't gain anything. Not if she stood for ten years. What fun it all is. This is marvellous.

PHILIP: (*to* ISOBEL) I am sorry, my heart, I haven't even asked if you consent? Don't refuse me. (*Kisses her hand*) Each gesture makes me happier and healthier. I will give the necessary orders immediately. There is no need to keep our engagement secret. My parents will be pleased . . . the Lord Chamberlain . . . the kind Lord Chamberlain will be delighted. The court . . . it will be a load off everyone's mind. Really the atmosphere was becoming impossible, I know. (*To* IVONA) Still standing? Surely everything is straight between us. What are you waiting for, my dear?

SIMON: She won't move, not by herself.

PHILIP: Call that lover of hers, let him cart her away, remove her from here to wherever it is she lives.

SIMON: I will get him at once and we will pack her off. Immediately, Philip, so she doesn't have a chance by just staying on.

PHILIP: Don't worry. (SIMON *leaves*) You can stand as long as
you like, you won't get me again into another absurd mess. I
have changed and everything has changed with me. There you
stand — a living reproach — but it means nothing to me. Stand
as much as you like. Ha, ha, ha. Anyhow, you like to be hurt
because you're sexless, you dislike yourself, you are your own
enemy. You subconsciously provoke people. You make everyone turn against you, so that everyone feels a knave and a thief.
But if you stand there for a year, difficult and gloomy, you can
do nothing against this ease. (*Smiles lightheartedly at* IVONA,
then turns ISOBEL *round*)

ISOBEL: Wouldn't it be better not to tell her all this? Have some
pity, Philip.

PHILIP: No, no pity now. Only pleasure. I know her from experience. Above all, one must keep talking as long as she is here,
one must keep telling her the worst things in the lightest
possible tone. This is the point — the more unpleasant, or
indecent the matter, the more innocent the manner; making
light of the whole thing. In this way her very existence is
discouraged, her silence not allowed to speak. She cannot put
anyone under an obligation. It places her in a world where she
can do nothing. Don't worry about me, I am safe now. It really
is very easy to break things off, it is only a question of chang-
ing the key. Let her stand, by all means let her stand and stare.
Let us go. It has not struck me before that one can simply leave
her behind. If she is staying, we will go. (IVONA *stoops*) Don't
curtsey to me.

IVONA: I am not curtseying.

PHILIP: Let it go. What did you pick up? A hair? What do you
want it for? It's Isobel's. Drop it.

IVONA: (*silent*)

Enter SIMON *and* INNOCENT.

INNOCENT: I am sorry but you can't do this. First Your Highness

made the girl fall in love with you and now you are sending her
away. Royal fancy. You broke her heart, I protest.

PHILIP: Oh, you protest?

INNOCENT: Or rather, I am trying to protest. (*Sits down abruptly
under* PRINCE'*s threatening stare*)

PHILIP: Look how this man sat on his protest.

SIMON: He sat on it as a dog on his tail. Off with you now —
take your ladylove and off with you both. Go.

PHILIP: Wait — she must give up that hair.

SIMON: Hair, Sir?

PHILIP: Give me that hair, Ivona, do you hear?

ISOBEL: Philip, I have enough hair. . . .

PHILIP: No, she must give it back. I can't stand her taking it with
her. (*Recovers the hair from* IVONA) I've got it. But that's not
enough. It is not the hair — it is us, she has still got us. (*To*
ISOBEL) We are still in her, the trap. Go on, I will come in a
moment. Simon. (*All leave except* SIMON) Stop her from
leaving the castle. Don't let her go. For the moment my breaking it off must not be made public. Let everything appear to be
just as before.

SIMON: I knew it. I knew that she would get you again if we let
her stand.

PHILIP: I want it to end for good. Don't get alarmed. I will have
to. . . (*Makes a gesture of cutting somebody's throat*)

SIMON: What? Whom?

PHILIP: Ivona.

SIMON: You are only working yourself up. It's all over. You have
broken it off. We will send her home and forget about her very
existence.

PHILIP: She won't be here, but she will be somewhere else.
Wherever she is she exists. I will be here, she will still be

somewhere. . . . Ugh . . . no, I can't stand it. I would much
rather kill her once and for all.

SIMON: But you are cured.

PHILIP: I am, really, I give you my word. I have fallen in love
with Isobel. I have shaken off the sufferings of that wretch. But
she still has us involved, Isobel and me, and she will go on, in
that way of hers — you know what I mean — involving us. I
can't stand it. I must kill. What if she goes away? She will
carry us with her. I know that it isn't normal practice to kill
people. But I assure you that I am absolutely sober. I know
what I am saying, I am not exaggerating one way or another.
(*Slightly anxious*) You must admit, I do not even look excited,
do I?

SIMON: Do you really want to kill her? You mean — kill, just
like that? It is a crime, you know?

PHILIP: It will be my last extravaganza, last escapade, the last
fling to finish it all. I will play it light, cool and easy — you
will see. It seems terrible, but in fact it is like an operation, no
more. It must be the easiest thing possible, to kill such a
weakling and she is asking for it. Will you promise to help me?

SIMON: What it is she is making you do, the bitch.

PHILIP: We have got into this mess and we have to get out of it.
We will keep my engagement to Isobel secret for the moment.
Don't tell anybody about it. Let everything appear as before . . .
till tomorrow. Tomorrow I shall devise the most convenient
method of extermination. But you must help me. I can't do it
alone. I must do it with somebody. I won't do it by myself.

ACT FOUR

A room in the castle. Trumpets etc. Enter the KING, *followed by three* DIGNITARIES.

KING: (*absentmindedly*) All right, all right. Stop pestering me. I have got important matters to attend to. Anything else?

CHANCELLOR: Your Majesty has still to decide what clothes would be appropriate for the ambassador extraordinary and minister plenipotentiary we are sending to France. Should he wear court dress or uniform?

KING: (*gloomily*) Let him go stark naked. (DIGNITARIES *shocked*) I am sorry, I am a little absentminded today. Let him go just as he likes. So long as he is paying for it himself, of course.

DIGNITARIES: This is the decision we had expected Your Majesty would take in your superior wisdom.

MARSHAL: Your Majesty, we are having tonight a great banquet to celebrate the occasion of the inspiring and democratic bethrothal of Prince Philip to the flower of the lowest social strata of our society, Miss Ivona Hopit. Has Your Majesty any special directives regarding the Menu?

KING: Give 'em pigswill. (DIGNITARIES *shocked*) I meant to say, of course, serve game. That's it, game will do very well. What are you staring at me for?

DIGNITARIES: This is just the decision we had expected Your Majesty would take in your superior wisdom.

SUPREME JUDGE: Your Majesty, may I humbly submit this petition, begging your clemency on behalf of old Plimsoll. It is signed by all the twelve courts from the lowest to the highest.

KING: Clemency be damned! Let him hang.

DIGNITARIES: Your Majesty!

KING: Hang him, I said. Why are you staring at me again? The prerogative of mercy is mine to use just as I like; I make use of it by not using it. I want that scoundrel to hang not because he is a scoundrel but because I. . . . Hm. . . . What I want to say is that we are all scoundrels. You, I, everybody. And now stop staring at me. I have had enough of it. As from today nobody is going to be allowed to stare at me. There is far too much staring going on altogether.

DIGNITARIES: This is precisely the decision we had expected Your Majesty to make in your superior wisdom.

KING: And now — out with you. Enough of all this twaddle. And don't try to wonder about it. As from today nobody is going to wonder at anything. I have been too gentle with you up to now. From today I shall show you who is master round here! I am going to muzzle the whole lot of you. (DIGNITARIES *bow*) Don't bow. I forbid you. Don't you know any better than to bow? Out!

DIGNITARIES *leave in a panic. The* KING *looks round with suspicion and hides behind a sofa. Enter* LORD CHAMBERLAIN, *looks round equally suspiciously, and starts to move furniture around in a furtive and sly manner. He pushes an armchair, turns up a corner of a carpet, disarranges books on the shelves, drops a plum stone on the floor. He notices the* KING.

CHAMBERLAIN: Oh!

KING: Hump . . . humph.

CHAMBERLAIN: Your Majesty?

KING: It is me all right. What the hell are you doing here?

CHAMBERLAIN: I? Nothing.

KING: (*gloomily*) You're wondering why I am in this room, aren't you? Seems the fashion these days to wonder. I am hiding, you see. I am hiding. I am laying an ambush.

CHAMBERLAIN: Ambush, Sire, for whom?

KING: Nobody in particular. Ambush for fun. (*Laughing*) This room is next to the apartments of our Grumpy Dumpy. Margaret often comes here as well. (*Lamely*) Some of their goings on may be worth seeing, so I would see them for myself.

CHAMBERLAIN: See what?

KING: Margaret.

CHAMBERLAIN: Her Majesty?

KING: Her Majesty. I would like to see what she is like when she is alone. When nobody can see her. I have been living with her for so long and I really don't know anything about her. I believe she has something on her conscience, humph? Perhaps . . . perhaps she too? There is nothing she couldn't do. My head whirls when I think of it. Perhaps she is deceiving me. That's most likely — or something else; everything is possible. Everything, anything.

CHAMBERLAIN: Your Majesty . . . that sofa. . . .

KING: Keep quiet, you fool. One sofa is as good as another when one wants to hide. You, Lord Chamberlain . . . what were you doing — what are you doing here . . . moving the furniture and fiddling with bits and pieces?

CHAMBERLAIN: Just to. . . .

KING: Just to what, tell me. I am also here just to. . . .

CHAMBERLAIN: I am doing a tour of the castle and I am trying to make things a little difficult.

KING: Difficult?

CHAMBERLAIN: For instance (*Sitting down*) it is a little difficult to sit down when the chair is put this way. (*Demonstrates*) One may sit beside it instead.

KING: Why are you dropping plum stones on the floor, Lord Chamberlain?

CHAMBERLAIN: To make it a little difficult to walk, Your Majesty.

KING: Difficult to walk? (*Gloomily*) Aah, so she has managed to get your back up too? Dumpy Grumpy. (*Retreating*) It's nothing, what?

CHAMBERLAIN: Your Majesty, I am a man of the world and of certain standing. I abhor all this impudence, this insolence, this dissipation sprouting up everywhere. It goes on and on, I don't know where it will end.

KING: Yes, yes, insolence . . . getting worse. Dissipation. What? Do you remember, old friend? (*Nudges* LORD CHAMBERLAIN)

CHAMBERLAIN: I don't want to remember anything, Sire.

KING: He bowed to you as well as to me, you know. It's nothing. Dissipation increasing . . . insolence . . . well, well. And what if I jump from behind the sofa, as she passes and spring at her and frighten her, frighten her . . . one can do it to her, one can do anything to her, frighten her and strangle her — yes — kill her. We have killed one before, after all.

CHAMBERLAIN: Fi donc, Your Majesty.

KING: I am only telling you one can do anything with her . . . it does not matter with her. You can do just as you like.

CHAMBERLAIN: Your Majesty, this is out of the question. Heaven help us; as it is this court is already seething with gossip and intrigue. And now, to cap it all, Your Royal Majesty popping out from behind a sofa. The need for tact and savoir faire has never been greater than in present circumstances. On the other hand (*Laughs*) a certain solution has just occurred to me. (*Laughs*)

KING: Why are you laughing like an idiot?

CHAMBERLAIN: This is the solution. Your Majesties are giving a banquet today to celebrate this deplorable betrothal: now, if we served fish, fish full of bones, pike for instance? It is in season now, one could serve it in a cream sauce. (*Enter* CHECKERS) Leave.

KING: (*gloomily*) Out. Pike. . . .

CHAMBERLAIN: Pike. (*Laughs*)

KING: What do you mean — pike?

CHAMBERLAIN: Your Majesty — pike served at an official banquet! I don't know whether you have noticed that she is even more lost when there are many people around? And it is so easy — yesterday I only gave her one look, a little up and down look and she almost choked herself with a potato. If one were to serve pike, it is such a difficult fish to eat, so full of bones. . . And if one were to serve it at an official banquet, with so many people there — wouldn't it be an easy thing to choke on?

KING: My Lord Chamberlain (*Looks at* CHAMBERLAIN) it sounds silly. Pike?

CHAMBERLAIN: (*a little hurt*) I know it sounds silly. I wouldn't be telling you about it, Sire, if it weren't.

KING: (*scared*) My Lord Chamberlain, but what? If she really. . .? . . . could she really choke?

CHAMBERLAIN: (*haughtily*) Then Your Majesty believes that she could really. . . . But that would be so silly, didn't you say? And if by mere chance such a silly accident did occur, what could we possibly have to do with . . . such silliness?

KING: But didn't we? Didn't we talk about it?

CHAMBERLAIN: Oh, that was just talk. . . . (*Looks attentively at his nails*)

KING: Just talk? Ha, it can be done. I know how to do it. If we storm her from above, we attack her sharply enough, we can get away with anything, even so silly that nobody would suspect us. Why not carp? What? It shall be carp, Lord Chamberlain.

CHAMBERLAIN: Pike, pike.

KING: But why not carp? Or eel? I suppose pike will do from above. . . Hm. . . . (*Scared again*) Storm her from above.

CHAMBERLAIN: Yes indeed, Your Majesty. Charging at her in full
regalia.

KING: Yes, yes, full regalia, of course, plenty of light, lots of
people and magnificent clothes . . . splendour, grandeur and
glory, then one battle cry from above and she's had it. She will
choke to death for sure. And nobody will be any the wiser
because it is too silly. We will do it in the grand manner, bear
down on her from on high, not from below. Royally we'll kill
her. What! I can see the Queen, let's hide.

CHAMBERLAIN: But. . . .

KING: Let's hide, I want to have a look at her. (*They hide behind
the sofa. The* QUEEN *comes in holding a little bottle.* KING,
aside) What's that? (*Sticks his head out*)

CHAMBERLAIN: Tss. . . .

QUEEN *walks a few steps towards* IVONA'*s room, stops, takes
out a little book, groans quietly and covers her face with her
hand.*

KING: (*aside*) What is this? A book of grief?

CHAMBERLAIN: (*aside*) Tss. . . .

QUEEN: (*reads out*) I am alone (*repeats*) yes, I am alone, alone.
Nobody knows the secrets of my bosom, nobody. Nobody
knows my bosom at all. (*Reads*)
To you, my little notebook's reams
I trust my reveries and dreams.
My chaste thoughts are here for you,
Nobody guesses this is true.
(*Speaks*) Nobody guesses indeed. How terrible it is. How
terrible. Oh death. (*Lifts up the little bottle*) Oh, poison.

KING: (*aside*) Poison?

QUEEN: (*her face contorted with grief*) Let nobody guess. Let us
read on. Let these words strengthen our determination to do the
terrible deed. (*Reads*)
My people, you see me on the throne.
You see me when my crown is on.

You do not know what fumbles inside,
Perhaps you think it's only pride.
In fact in that too rich a frame
I grope towards another name.
Undone within, royal outside,
I would rather be a floppy bride
I want to be free as a bird on the wing
So that my verses may better sing.
Oh, suppleness, O pliability. Oh, I must burn this. Destroy it. It's
terrifying. And I wrote it. It's mine and whatever happens it still
is mine. Oh, I see now the whole horror of it. Ignatius, Ignatius
has read it. I see the likeness . . . I do. As she slobbers, gropes and
stumbles . . . she is herself a terrifying allusion to my poetry. She
is the informer, the betrayer. It's me, it's me, it's mine. There is a
likeness between us. Oh, how she has dragged it all out into the
open. How she has exposed it. Anyone who has seen her will
discover that likeness to Margaret. Anyone who looks at her will
know me as I really am just as if he read my most intimate lines.
Enough. She must perish. Margaret, Margaret, you have to put
her to death. Forward, murderous bottle. She must not continue
on this earth, there is no time left — otherwise everyone will
know about that poisonous link between us. I don't wish to
become the butt of ridicule, gossip and derision, the scapegoat of
suggestion. To death with her. Let us go quietly to her room and
put a few drops from this bottle into her medicine. Nobody will
know. She is such a weakling, they will think she has just died.
Who could guess it was me? I am the Queen. (*Moves on*) No, I
can't go like this. I can't look my ordinary self when I am about
to do murder. I must change, get my hair dishevelled at least, not
too much, nothing ostentatious, just enough to effect a change.
Like this.

KING: (*aside*) Tss. . . .

QUEEN: Shall I go so dishevelled? But that may betray you. If
anybody should catch you with your hair all over the place. Stop
talking to yourself. I am sure she also talks to herself. Margaret,
stop talking to yourself. It may give you away. (*Looks into a
mirror*) This glass is showing me up. I can't go on like this. I must
bring all my ugliness into the open before I am ready to go. Stop

talking to yourself. Somebody will hear you. I can't stop talking to myself. Do all murderers talk to themselves before the act? There is something odd, abnormal about this room — a sort of venemous disorder? A twisted mouth, Margaret, that's what is needed. That's better, let's go now. You and I together. But am I not going alone? Twist your mouth more. Let us go. Remember all your lines and go. Remember all your pliable reveries and go. Remember the suppleness, the secret striving suppleness and go. I am going. I can't . . . it is too insane. A moment longer, let us put on a little smear . . . the ink here. . . . (*Smears some ink on her face*) Now it's going to be much easier . . . I am different. Stop, this may betray you. Let us go, to kill the informer. Let us read the poem again, just a moment longer (*Takes out her book of poems*) to inflame the desire to murder.

KING: (*jumps up*) Margaret!

QUEEN: Ignatius. . . .

KING: I have caught you redhanded. Show it to me. (*Wants to take her book*)

QUEEN: Let me go.

KING: Let me see it. Now. Oh, murderess. I want all your secret sins. Let me see and we shall start another honeymoon. Let me see, you secret poisoner.

QUEEN: Ah. (*Faints*)

CHAMBERLAIN: Water, water. She has fainted.

KING: Ha. Now we know. She dreams of suppleness and wants to poison Grumpy Dumpy. It doesn't matter anyhow, I have killed her already.

QUEEN: (*faintly*) You killed her? Whom?

KING: I have drowned her. I and our Chamberlain. We have drowned her together.

CHAMBERLAIN: Water. Here is some water.

QUEEN: You have drowned? Ivona?

KING: Silly. Not Ivona but it makes no difference. Not Ivona, another one. Long time ago. Now you know about me. You know? Compared to my crimes, all your silly little verses are just nothing. I have killed her and now I will kill Grumpy Dumpy. I will kill her too.

QUEEN: You will kill. . . .

KING: Yes, now I will kill her. If it comes off. Someone is doing it to someone else, somewhere, every minute of the day. All the time, if not this one then another. And if not that one, some-body else. You know? Charging from above with full regalia, intimidate, and then. . . . (*To* CHAMBERLAIN) Give me some water. (*Drinks*) I am old . . . I am getting older.

QUEEN: I won't let you, Ignatius. I forbid it.

KING: You will let me, old girl, you will, as you let yourself have a go, as everyone lets everyone else.

Enter IVONA, *wants to withdraw when she has seen the others but is unable to do it and proceeds to her room. From this moment everyone talks in whispers.*

KING: Ha!

QUEEN: Ignatius, I don't agree, I don't want you to. . . .

CHAMBERLAIN: Quiet, for goodness sake.

KING: Be quiet, you fool. (*To* CHAMBERLAIN) It will be all right. (*To* QUEEN) Do you think I would do it the way you planned, humbly, from below? Not on your life. I will kill her in style, in majesty, with a battle cry and yet so stupidly that nobody will be any the wiser. Margaret, a murder has to be high handed and not done meekly, cap in hand. Go and wash yourself, you are looking a sight. And get that banquet going. It is getting late. We will have pike for the hors d'oeuvres by the way. I would like pike myself, in a cream sauce. Jolly good fish, pike, special. What?

QUEEN: Pike. . .? Pike? (*To* CHAMBERLAIN) He has gone mad. Thank God.

KING: Hold your tongue. I haven't gone mad. Give us pike as I tell you.

CHAMBERLAIN: Madam, pike makes an excellent hors d'oeuvre, I can't see any reason why one shouldn't serve pike.

QUEEN: I am not going to serve pike. Don't drive me out of my mind, I am not going to serve anything of the sort. Why pike? It's unheard of, the whole thing. Why should I serve pike?

KING: What! Temper! (*To* CHAMBERLAIN) Give me the crown. (*Puts it on*)

QUEEN: (*terrified*) Ignatius, Ignatius, why? Take it off.

KING: Margaret, if I tell you to serve pike you will serve pike. Don't bicker or I will crown you. I can crown you. I can crown you for I am a sinner. I can do anything and you tremble before me for I am a sinner. I am the king of sin, get that, I am the king of rot and sin, of rape and groan.

QUEEN: (*terrified*) Ignatius.

KING: Oh well. . . . Now, now . . . serve pike. Invite all the elderly statesmen, all those old experienced intimidators, you know, the old boys who would paralyse the devil himself with fright. (*In a lower voice*) Margaret, enough of all this shyness, fear, shame, do you understand? Enough poetry, flexibility, pliability. You are not a chicken, you are a lady, the Queen. You should not flop. The others have to bend, not you, remember. Now go and wash yourself, you are looking like nothing on earth, you slattern. Put on your damask dress — show what you can do, old girl. Get a move on. Pull yourself together — a gracious bearing and tact and a royal manner — a general refinement is what you are for, after all. Tell your wenches to put on their best front too. Now, get along — you understand? You have to put up a first class performance, you and your women — they are to be ladies and not sluts. Get the guests and the food and don't bother about the rest, I will deal with that. And remember — grandly, grandly, royally. One, two, three — majesty. Now go, you slavey. (*Exit the* QUEEN, *covering her face*) Lord Chamberlain. . . . (*Nudges him*)

CHAMBERLAIN: Sire?

KING: (*in a whisper, gloomily*) Bow to me. I need you to bow.

CHAMBERLAIN: (*listening*) Somebody is coming.

KING: We'd better hide.

They hide behind the sofa. Enter, creeping, PHILIP *carrying a knife, followed by* SIMON *carrying a basket.*

PHILIP: Where has she gone?

SIMON: Tss, here.

PHILIP: What is she doing?

SIMON: (*looking into* IVONA'*s room*) Swotting flies.

PHILIP: Swotting?

SIMON: Yawning.

PHILIP: (*getting his knife ready*) Let us try. . . . One, two, three. See that nobody is coming. Get your basket ready.

SIMON *opens the basket,* PHILIP *creeps towards* IVONA'*s door.*

KING: (*aside to* CHAMBERLAIN) Our Phil is at it as well.

CHAMBERLAIN: Tss. . . .

SIMON: (*who has been observing* PHILIP) Philip, stop. Or I will give the alarm.

PHILIP: Nervous?

SIMON: It's impossible. Going for that wretch with a knife. It's too silly — one can't do it. You can't knife somebody like that. And this basket.

PHILIP: Stop. (*Puts the knife down*) Technically, the basket is indispensable.

SIMON: If only you could see yourself.

PHILIP: Enough.

SIMON: (*looking into* IVONA'*s room*) Going to sleep. May be asleep now. . . .

PHILIP: Asleep?

SIMON: Looks like it. She is lolling in her chair.

PHILIP: (*looking in*) Now or never. If now it would be painless. You try.

SIMON: Me?

PHILIP: It's easier for you — you are a stranger and you are an equal. You are not her target . . . she does not love you. Simon, do it for me. It won't take more than a second. It's an operation — she won't feel anything. She won't even know that in the same second that you do it, she won't exist any more. It will happen outside her, it is easy, it is our act and it does not concern her really.

SIMON: That's what makes it difficult: it is too easy. (*Takes the knife*)

PHILIP: No, no, no.

SIMON: No?

PHILIP: It is as if you were about to slaughter a hen.

SIMON: Can't we? I had thought we could but we can't. Oh, damn it all, she is too weak, too sickly . . . if only she were a stout, red-cheeked wench but she is so pale. One can't do it to one so pale, can one?

PHILIP: Somebody is watching us.

SIMON: I am watching.

PHILIP: No, it's somebody else — who sees everything.

SIMON: I see it, of course.

PHILIP: Yes, you see me and I see you. You better go now, I prefer to be on my own. I will deal with it. An operation, rather horrid perhaps but still an operation. I would rather be a monster for a moment than for a lifetime. Go behind the door, I will do it. . . . (*Exit* SIMON) On my own. It really is salvation for her, isn't it? The end of suffering. And for me as well. The whole thing is perfectly rational. . . . (*Looks round, takes up the knife, puts it down again*) Simon!

KING: (*aside, very excited*) You are a bungler.

SIMON: Yes? (*Returns*)

PHILIP: It is even worse on one's own. The thing looms so
   large . . . swelling and growing horribly. What's that?

SIMON: She is breathing. . . . (*They both listen*)

PHILIP: Breathing. . . . (*Looks into* IVONA'*s room*) breathing,
   alive, all of her together, in herself, up to her eyes, immersed,
   contained in herself. (*Takes the knife*) Easy enough to push this
   into the flesh . . . the problem will still be there . . . unresolved.
   It's horribly easy and that makes it so horribly difficult.

   Enter ISOBEL.

ISOBEL: What is this? (*At the sight of the knife*) Murder!

PHILIP & SIMON: Tss. . . .

ISOBEL: Murder . . . would'st thou be a murderer?

PHILIP: Keep quiet and don't interfere. I am settling a few
   personal matters and I will come to you when I am ready. Go
   now.

ISOBEL: (*to* SIMON) You too? Are you the accomplice?

SIMON: It's mad, Philip. Let us leave it.

KING: (*aside*) Mad indeed.

ISOBEL: Come away, I beseech you.

PHILIP: (*looking into* IVONA'*s room*) Asleep. . . .

ISOBEL: Let her sleep. What is that to you that she is asleep? I
   too will sleep . . . tonight, Philip.

PHILIP: Sshh. A sigh.

ISOBEL: I too will sigh . . . tonight. Don't think of her. I am here.
   Don't think of her, don't murder her. Come away, Philip.

PHILIP: Dreaming, what dreams?

ISOBEL: Let her be. I will tell you of my dream last night. I
   dreamed of you. Come, please.

PHILIP: About me, about us. She must be dreaming about us. About you and me. You and I are in there.

ISOBEL: In there? In what?

PHILIP: In her, inside, within. Don't you hear she is in pain, painfully asleep! Her breathing sounds cruel. It is hard labour with the two of us inside. She can get up to all sorts of things. Goodness knows what she will do with us.

ISOBEL: You are not yourself, Philip. You have lost touch again.

PHILIP: (*still whispering*) I am myself but I can't be myself altogether, how can I get back to norm if she stays outside it? And from outside she plays the tune and we dance to it. Trala . . . la, tralala.

ISOBEL: How can you, Philip, after what happened between us?

PHILIP: (*listening*) Snoring. . . .

ISOBEL: What?

PHILIP: Snoring.

ISOBEL: This is really too much.

KING: (*aside*) Too much. Too much, damn it. Get on! Over and done with!

PHILIP: (*answering without realising it*) I can't. What is this? Who said that? Have you noticed, there is something odd about this room? Look at the furniture. (*Knocks over a chair*)

KING: Odd, huh, odd.

CHAMBERLAIN: Tss. . . .

SIMON: Let us kill her now or let us go. I really can't stand here for ever with this basket. I will go, I will run away from here. I won't be an accessory, no longer.

PHILIP: I must, I must.

KING: On with it, man.

ISOBEL: Kiss me. (*To* SIMON) Make him kiss me.

PHILIP: (*listening*) She's gurgling.

ISOBEL: I have had enough. I am going.

SIMON: Your Highness, do kiss her. For heavens sake do something to make him kiss you.

KING: Go on, kiss her.

CHAMBERLAIN: Tss. . . .

ISOBEL: I am not going to beg for a kiss. I am not going to stand for hours outside the door of that wretch with a basket and a knife. It is too much. I leave you for ever.

PHILIP: (*desperately*) Don't leave me, Isobel. I will kiss you. Wait.

ISOBEL: (*pushing him away*) I won't. Let me go. I won't kiss to order. It doesn't make sense, outside this door, with this basket, with this knife. I won't. I am going and going for good.

KING: (*still behind the sofa*) Go on. Get on with it.

PHILIP: Keep cool or we will all go demented. Be quiet and don't wake her up. Little patience, Isobel, you are too impetuous. I mustn't lose you. Don't bother about me not being myself, I agree that one should not really kiss in these circumstances, outside this door, but let us, let us kiss one another as if it were the most natural thing to do. If we can't be ourselves let us at least pretend we are, otherwise we shall never escape. A kiss now will be our salvation, it will bring us back to norm, it will get us out of this predicament, I am sure. (*Embraces* ISOBEL) I love you. Say that you love me.

ISOBEL: I won't. I won't say it for anything. Let me go.

PHILIP: She loves me. I love her.

IVONA *appears at the door rubbing her eyes. The* KING *excited, leans out from behind the sofa and is held down by the* CHAMBERLAIN.

KING: Go on, Philip.

ISOBEL: Philip. . . .

PHILIP: (*passionately, directing her*) Philip. Philip, I love you.

SIMON: Philip, she is awake.

KING: (*loudly*) Now, Philip, now. Go ahead. Give it to her. Down with Grumpy Dumpy.

CHAMBERLAIN: Hold the King.

ISOBEL: Let us run.

KING: Don't scream. Get me out of here. (*Scrambles out*) Ugh, I am stiff, I have got pins and needles. (*To* PHILIP) Go on. Quick. Don't botch it in the end. We will bump her off, it's now or never. This way, Chamberlain. We are off.

Enter the QUEEN *dressed for the banquet. The footmen bring in the lights and the tables are laid for the feast. They are followed by the* GUESTS.

KING: Wait. This is no good. We forgot the pike. Of course, from above, not from below. From on high, not cap in hand. Grandly, in majesty; intimidate and overwhelm. Margaret, it's your turn, bear down on her. (*To the* GUESTS) Delighted . . . delighted . . . how kind . . . get your collar straight, Philip and tidy your hair. Royally, imperially, my son. (*To* CHAMBERLAIN) Give me the crown.

PHILIP: What is all this?

CHAMBERLAIN: Nothing, it is only the banquet.

KING: (*to the* GUESTS) Let me greet you all. Come in. Come in.

GUESTS: Your Majesty.

QUEEN: Come in. We are delighted.

GUESTS: Your Majesty. (*Bows and curtseys*)

KING: (*to the* GUESTS) And now, down to it. Let the superior gnaw at the inferior and the inferior at the superior — or rather let the superior draw out of the inferior the rightful pride and the inferior from the superior — the stimulus and the incentive to more fruitful efforts and noble rivalry and finally in conclusion I would just like to ask you to place my future

daughter-in-law opposite us, as it is indeed in her honour that
we are giving this . . . fête champêtre.

GUESTS: (*bows and curtseys*)

QUEEN: Whether you will sit high or low, let everybody flourish
and shine in the sunlight of our graciousness. Let the ladies
show themselves at their best, let the men surpass themselves.
Let us all be brilliant, elegant, distinguished and altogether
remarkable.

KING: Indeed. In full cry. Tally ho. What . . . let us sit down, of
course.

GUESTS: Your Majesty. (*Bows and curtseys.* KING *and* QUEEN *sit
down*)

CHAMBERLAIN: (*to* IVONA) Be gracious enough to take your seat,
Madam. (IVONA *does not budge*) Will you be so kind as to sit
down. (*Puts* IVONA *on the chair*) Your Highness, will you come
here? And Your Eminence? And Your Excellency? And you,
Countess Dowager . . . and you, maître? (*All sit down*)

KING: As we have said, we are giving this modest but elegant
entertainment to celebrate the violent end . . . I mean, the
happy betrothal of our future daughter in law. We have decided
that it would be fitting to grace the occasion by bestowing upon
her the title of the Princess of Burgundia, in partibus
infidelium, of course. She is the centre of tonight's festivities.
Look, how nicely she acknowledges it all.

GUESTS: Your Majesty. (*Discreet clapping*)

KING: (*serving himself*) A little bony perhaps, but tasty I think.

QUEEN: (*serving herself*) Getting on a little but very, very distinguished, I think, especially in this sauce. I find distinction
much more important than what is normally described as
poetry, don't you? Perhaps I am not sentimental enough but I
really can't stand (*Very grandly*) all that poetic diction — birds,
songs and the rest of it. It is all too, too childish and I much
prefer truly mature pursuits becoming to a lady of my position,
a lady pur sang.

GUESTS: Aha!

CHAMBERLAIN: (*serving himself*) This fish looks fairly ordinary at the first glance, but how truly aristocratic it is in its very essence. What a splendid sauce. It's like cream and yet different and so superior. The taste is piquant, sharp, brilliant, paradoxical and paradisial. I don't doubt that this distinguished gathering will do it justice.

GUESTS: Aha!

KING: (*to* IVONA) Don't you like it? (*Threatening*) Don't you?

CHAMBERLAIN: (*icily*) You must be suffering from a singular lack of appetite, Madam?

GUESTS: (*shocked*) Oh.

IVONA: (*starts eating*)

KING: (*gloomily to* IVONA) If you are not careful with this fish you might choke. Those things happen, you know. A pike like this seems innocent enough but sometimes. . . .

CHAMBERLAIN: (*to* IVONA) As His Majesty has just been kind enough to observe, one should be careful when eating pike or one may choke. (*Sharply*) It's dangerous. It's a difficult fish.

KING: (*menacingly*) Dangerous, I say.

GUESTS: (*amazed*) Oh. (*Stop eating, silence*)

QUEEN: (*elegantly*) Eh bien, Ivonne, vous ne mangez pas, ma chère?

CHAMBERLAIN: (*fixing his eye glass*) You despise it? The pike of His Majesty is not good enough for you?

KING: (*more menacing still*) What does this behaviour mean?

IVONA: (*starts eating 'solo'*)

KING: (*gets up, points menacingly to* IVONA) She has choked. A bone in her throat . . . a bone, I say. No. . . .

IVONA: (*chokes*)

GUESTS: (terrified, stand up) Help. Water. Thump her on the back.

QUEEN: Help.

GUESTS: Oh, the unfortunate maid. What a thing. Catastrophe. Caput. Dead. Let us not disturb their Majesties . . . the family. . . . (They leave, exposing the body in full view)

PHILIP: Dead?

CHAMBERLAIN: Choked on a bone.

PHILIP: Bone? Ah yes, a bone. I see. . . . She looks dead enough. (Silence)

QUEEN: (nervous, perhaps slightly embarrassed) Ignatius, we must start thinking about the court mourning. You haven't got a suitable suit. You have put on weight and they are all too small.

KING: I haven't, have I? Well, I will order one.

QUEEN: Yes, but you must send for the tailor straight away.

KING: (surprised) Tailor? Yes, of course. . . . (Rubs his eyes) Yes, Solomon, the Tailor, men's outfitters. (Looks at IVONA) What? Dead? I mean — really dead.

QUEEN: (after a moment) We shall all die. . . .

KING: (after another moment) Do something. One must do something. One must say something, surely. To deal with the silence. So, Philip, you must be brave. She is dead. You can't help it.

QUEEN: (patting PHILIP on the head) Your Mother is with you, son.

PHILIP: What are you saying?

CHAMBERLAIN: (to the servants, pointing to the body) Take her and put her on the bed. Run, one of you, and get the bed ready. Get Cadaver at once, the funeral director. We can't do without him. He is our key man in this. Go and get him. (The servants draw nearer to the body) Wait, I will kneel. (Kneels down)

KING: Yes, of course. (*Kneels down*) This is the right thing. One should kneel. (*They all kneel down except* PHILIP) We should have done it straight away.

PHILIP: Sorry? What are you doing?

CHAMBERLAIN: What are we doing? (PHILIP *is silenced*) Will you, please, kneel?

QUEEN: Kneel, Philippe. All should be on their knees. And we all are.

KING: Get down. You can't stand up when we are all on our knees. (PHILIP *kneels down*)

THE MARRIAGE

Translated by Louis Iribarne

Excerpt from an Interview about *The Marriage* given by Witold Gombrowicz in 1968

It was still wartime when I started work on *The Marriage*. It gestated slowly, by fits and starts, during my time in the Argentine: *Faust* and *Hamlet* were my models, but only because of their quality of genius. I wanted to write a play which was 'great' and 'inspired', so I went back to those works which in my youth I had read with veneration. And my ambitions were not without a certain guile. I craftily figured that to write a masterpiece was easier than writing just an ordinarily good play. It seemed a lot less hard to be a genius.

Why was this? *The Marriage*, like all my works a revolt against form, is a travesty of form, a parody of 'great drama'. But if I was going to send up 'genius', couldn't I also steal a little of it for myself? Who could tell whether I had stolen it or not?. . .

I wanted to show humanity on its way from the Church of God to the Church of man. Yet I didn't start off with this idea. At first, I started by throwing into the scene a handful of ideas, of images and situations and slowly, haltingly, I evolved this main idea. When I'd come to the middle of the second act, I still didn't know what I wanted. And the stumbling creation of my *Missa Solemnis* which resembled a drunk or sleep-walker or madman while rising out of the short circuits of form, its connections and combinations, its rhymes and interior rhythms, seemed similar to the development of History, which also lurches forward like a drunk or madman.

Then I wrote:

JOHNNY — No.
HENRY — Nothing.
THE FATHER — It's been transformed.
THE MOTHER — Distorted.
JOHNNY— Destroyed.
HENRY— Dislocated.

and I suddenly burst into tears like a child. Nothing like it had ever happened to me before — I was hysterical!

I wept bitterly, soaking the paper in front of me. It was not so much the fact that the words evoked my personal misfortunes that filled me with despair, but that they came so easily to me. I experienced their rhyme and rhythm like a sharp, stabbing pain. I wept with horror at the internal coherence of my misery. Then I stopped crying and I started to write.

D.F.   What happened to *The Marriage*?

W.G.   I translated it into Spanish with the help of my friend Alexander Roussowitch and thanks to the help of Cecilia Debenedetti and Stanislas Odyniec, it was published in Buenos Aires. The artistic circles of that capital ignored it. In 1963, Jorge Lavelli, a young Argentine director living in Paris, became interested in it. He mounted an excellent production at the Théâtre Récamier, which was the starting point of his rapid rise to fame as a director. After a time, *The Marriage* found a great director in the shape of Alf Sjöberg, who did a production at the Royal Dramatic Theatre of Stockholm. Sjöberg put a lot of work and passion into the rehearsals of both *The Marriage* and *Princess Ivona* and they were a great success. The third of the better productions of *The Marriage* took place at the Schillertheater in Berlin where there were fifty-one curtain calls at the preview. I owe a great deal to the director, Ernst Schroder, to his excellent company and in particular to Helmut Griem. Alas, through a set of unfortunate circumstances I didn't see one of these productions. To be honest, I haven't set foot in a theatre for thirty years. I write plays but I don't go to the theatre . . . I don't know why. . . . Laziness, perhaps.

D.R.   How do you compare your plays with Beckett's or Ionesco's?

W.G.   I don't compare them. The critics do that. When *Princess Ivona* and *The Marriage* were produced in Paris, they said they belonged to Beckett's and Ionesco's 'theatre of the absurd'. But *Princess Ivona* was written in 1936, *The Marriage* in 1946, when no-one had heard of these writers. And also, my theatre isn't absurd.

Yes, *The Marriage* is obscure and dream-like and fantastical: because it is so full of shadows, I wouldn't know how to analyse it fully myself. I like the director to let this kind of sphinx evolve its own form freely — to cry out, to wander — so long as he is careful about the semi-musical harmony of the ceremonial. Nevertheless, *The Marriage* has an action which holds together and there is no reason for it not to be perceptible to the audience. You see, as I wanted these conversations to be a kind of clue to my works, I am going to tell you what *The Marriage* is about. Perhaps it will be useful to some director.

What *The Marriage* is about

The Marriage is a dream. A dream of Henry, a Polish soldier in the last war somewhere in France in the French army fighting the Germans. At the core of this dream are the anxieties of Henry for his family, lost down there at the bottom of Poland but also the most essential anxieties of contemporary man on the wrong side of two eras.

Surging into Henry's thoughts are his birthplace in Poland, his parents, his fiancée Mary. The house is degraded, here it is turned into an inn. Mary has become Molly, a serving girl, a barmaid. The father is the barman.

The father is pursued by drunks. Then comes the key-scene: to defend his human dignity, the father shouts out that he is 'untouchable'.

'A king, a king, an untouchable king,' sneer the drunks.

And Henry pays homage to his father, who changes into a king. And not only does the father-king raise Henry to princely dignity, but he promises him as well a sacred and worthy marriage by means of his royal power, a marriage which will restore Molly, the barmaid, to her purity and integrity of yesteryear. . . .

The first act finishes there. It seems that human dignity is saved.

In the second act, preparations are made for this 'worthy and holy' marriage to be solemnized by a bishop. But doubts start to infiltrate into Henry's dream. This whole ceremony of marriage starts to wobble, as if threatened by Stupidity — as if he, Henry, striving with all his soul to be wise, dignified and pure, lacks confidence in himself and his dream.

The chief drunk again bursts into the room, pissed as a newt! Henry is about to come to blows with him, when suddenly (as it happens in dreams) the scene changes into a reception at Court. The drunk is turned into the Ambassador of an enemy power, who incites Henry to treason.

'Betray your father the king,' is more or less what the drunk says, 'the Bishop, King, Church and God are only old superstitions. Proclaim yourself king and then authority, divine or otherwise, will no longer be necessary to you, you will give yourself the sacrament of marriage and force everybody to recognize it and recognize Molly as pure and married to you.'

Such is the key to the metaphor of *The Marriage*, the transition from a world founded on divine and paternal authority to another where Henry's will becomes the divine, creative will . . . like Hitler's or Stalin's.

Henry yields to the blandishments of the drunk. He dethrones his father and becomes king himself.

There follows a scene where the drunk asks Johnny, Henry's friend, to hold a flower over Molly's head: Johnny does so, the drunk pinches it, leaving Johnny and Molly in a compromising position, which no flower could justify. A terrible thought arises in Henry's mind that Molly . . . and Johnny. . . .

> You pig!
> You've bound them together
> By a dreadful
> And inferior bond.
> You've married them
> You pig priest,

he screams.

End of Act Two.

In Act Three, Henry is dictator, who has tamed everybody, even his parents. The marriage preparations are gone through a second time, but this time without God or any sanction other than his absolute power.

Yet he feels that his power will have no meaning unless confirmed by someone making a voluntary sacrifice of his blood. That is why he urges Johnny to commit suicide for him. This sacrifice will appease his jealousy, make him strong and powerful enough to go through with the marriage . . . and Molly's purity (and also to fulfil the dream . . . all that he has been looking for since the start). Johnny agrees to this plan.

In the final scene, Johnny kills himself. But Henry weakens and recoils horrified at what he has done.

The marriage will not be fulfilled.

From an interview with Dominique de Roux
in Entretiens with Gombrowicz,
Editions Piere Belford, 1968
Translanted by Jonathan Hammond

The Marriage was first performed in January 1964, at the Théâtre Récamier in Paris. The cast was as follows:

FRANK father and king	Alexis Nitzer
KATHARINE mother and queen	Juliette Brac
HENRY son and prince	Olivier Lebeaut
JOHNNY friend and courtier	Francois Mirante
MOLLY servant and princess	Claudine Raffalli
DRUNKARD	Fernand Berset
CHANCELLOR	Luc Delhumeau
CHAMBERLAIN)	
CHIEF OF POLICE)	Augy Hayter
BISHOP PANDULF)	
DIGNITARY/TRAITOR)	Andre Cazalas

The play was directed by Jorge Lavelli

This translation of *The Marriage* was broadcast on 21 March 1969, on BBC Radio 3. The cast was as follows:

FRANK	Maurice Denham
KATHARINE	Mary Morris
HENRY	Frank Finlay
JOHNNY	Christopher Guinee
MOLLY	Angela Pleasance
DRUNKARD	Felix Felton
CHANCELLOR	Lockwood West
CHAMBERLAIN	Frederick Treves
CHIEF OF POLICE	Francis de Wolff
BISHOP PANDULF	James Thomason
DIGNITARY/TRAITOR	Michael Deacon

The play was directed by H.B. Fortuin.

ACT ONE

An oppressive, forlorn landscape. In the shadows, ruins of a disfigured church.

HENRY: The curtain has risen. . . . An obscure church . . . .
An incongruous ceiling. . . . A strange vault. . . .
And the sign slips into the abyss of the abyss
Of the sphere of spheres, and stone and stone. . . .

Through an entrance that has never been entered
Stands a deformed altar of a foreign Psalter
Clasped shut by the absurdity of the chalice
That sinking into stillness gouges out the pastor. . . .

A void. A desert. Nothing, I am alone here
Alone
Alone

But perhaps I am not alone; who knows what is behind me,
perhaps . . . something . . . someone is standing here alongside
me, off to the side, off to the side, some id . . . some insuperable,
ungovernable, idiotized, idiotouchable idiot, who can touch
and . . . . (*With alarm*) I'd better not move . . . no, don't move,
because if we move . . . he'll move . . . and touch. . . . (*With
growing uneasiness*) Oh, if only something or someone would
come out from somewhere. . . . Aha! There's something. . . .

JOHNNY *emerges from the shadows.*

Johnny! It's Johnny!

JOHNNY: Henry!

HENRY: Imagine what a horrible dream I had
I dreamt I saw some hideous monster, and
I wanted to run, but couldn't!

JOHNNY: That stew they give us for supper is pretty
Tough and indigestible. I have nightmares too
Sometimes. . . .

HENRY: But at least you are of flesh and blood. Or perhaps
you're only a dream too. . . . What are you doing here, anyway?

JOHNNY: Don't ask me.

HENRY: Johnny, Johnny, why are you so frightfully sad?

JOHNNY: And you, why are you so sad?

HENRY: No special reason.

JOHNNY: No special reason.

HENRY: Something strange has happened to us. Where are we?
I'm afraid this place is under a curse . . . and we're under a
curse too. . . . Excuse me if my words sound artificial. . . . I'm
unable to speak naturally. . . .

> A hundredfold sorrow
> A grief without cease or limit
> And a terrible oppression, dumb and dark,
> Have invaded my soul! Oh, God!
> Oh, God! Oh, God!

JOHNNY: (*petulantly*)
What do you need God for when I am here?
Don't you see, friend, that I am the same as you?
Why let yourself get upset by ghosts
If you and I are of flesh and blood
If you are as I and I am as you!

HENRY: (*joyously*) 'If you are as I and I am as you!' Oh, what's
the difference! But I'm very glad you're here, Johnny! With
you here it's a different story. But. . . . Where are we? All the
same I have the feeling . . . we're somewhere. . . . There . . .
there's something over there. . . .

Part of a wall becomes visible, some furniture, the outline of a room.

I've seen all this before somewhere.

JOHNNY: So have I. . . .

HENRY: (*dramatically*)
            We are somewhere
            We are somewhere. But where?
            What's that?

A room appears — the dining room of a country manor house in Poland that looks as though it has been transformed into a dive.

JOHNNY: (*hesitantly*) I swear this room reminds me of something. . . . It reminds me a little of your dining room in Maloszyce. It's similar and yet not similar. . . . That clock. That chest of drawers. There's the room I slept in when I came to visit you during the holidays. . . .

HENRY: Yes, but wait a minute — we're not in Maloszyce . . . we're stationed at the front in northern France — at the front in northern France — at the front in northern France. And if we're here, we can't be there!

JOHNNY: It's similar and yet not similar. . . . It would seem to be the same dining room, even though it does resemble a restaurant or a dive . . . or an inn . . . or a boardinghouse . . . or a tavern. . . .

HENRY: This room is disguised and everything is abnormal.

JOHNNY: Don't be silly, stop trying to complicate matters.
            What do you care if something's abnormal
            As long as we are normal!
            And these chairs are real, they're made of wood,
                and one is sure to find something in the cupboard.
            But why isn't anyone here? Hallo!

HENRY: (*terrified*) Don't shout! Wait! You'd better not shout!

JOHNNY: Why shouldn't I shout?
            Hallo! Is anybody here? Is everybody dead? Hallo!

HENRY: Fool! Shut your trap!
            Shhh! Be quiet, I say! Hallo!
            Why doesn't anybody come out? Shhh! Hallo!

JOHNNY: Hallo!

HENRY: Hallo!

JOHNNY: Hallo!

Enter the FATHER, *old, rigid, sclerotic, distrustful. . . .*

HENRY: At last, someone. . . . Excuse me, is this a restaurant? (*Silence*) Is this a restaurant?

FATHER: And what if it is?

HENRY: (*in the style of a traveller*)
             Tell me, is it possible
             To get a bite to eat here?

FATHER: (*in the style of an innkeeper*)
             I suppose so
             But by shouting you won't get anywhere.

HENRY: (*to* JOHNNY) That voice sounds familiar.

JOHNNY: He looks very similar to your father. . . . I swear it's him, though on second thoughts. . . . I'm not so sure. . . . It's hard to tell at first sight.

HENRY: You're crazy. If that were my father, he'd be the first to recognize us. No, come on, let's forget about it. That's not my father. Come on, let's sit down. (*To the* FATHER) Is this an inn? I mean, is it possible to get a room for the night here?

FATHER: (*grudgingly*) I suppose so, seeing as how we rent rooms here. But you better watch your p's and q's!

HENRY: Watch my p's and q's. . . .

FATHER: (*crescendo*)
             Be polite and respectful!

HENRY: Oh, I see, respectful. . . .

FATHER: (*shouting*)
             Civil and courteous!

Enter the MOTHER, *an elderly woman, worn out, dressed in rags. She joins in shouting with the* FATHER.

MOTHER: You'd better behave yourselves, and mind you no

hanky-panky, because we won't hold with that around here . . .
we'll have no part in that, thank you very much. . . .

JOHNNY: (*to* HENRY) That's your mother.

HENRY: (*loudly*)
>It would seem so
>But it's not altogether certain
>This is all a little confusing, but I shall
>Straighten everything out!

(*To* JOHNNY) Forgive me for speaking artificially, but I feel as
though I were in an artificial situation. (*Raises the lamp*)

>Come over here
>Come over here. . . . Come over here, I say

Come closer, that's it, closer! I swear, you'd think I were trying
to lure a bunch . . . a bunch of chickens. . . . Keep coming!
Closer! Look how grudgingly they come. Come a little closer
or else I shall have to come closer.

>I'll come closer, and as I come closer

You come closer. . . . My God, it's as though I were trying to
catch a bunch of fish. But why is it so quiet around here?

>My father has stepped out of the shadows
>But he's changed so much
>I can hardly recognize him
>And moreover so strangely silent that
>I must speak the whole time alone
>Alone must I speak until I'm transformed
>Into a priest of my father!
>And here comes my mother like a steamer
>To tell the truth she's not very similar to my mother
>Perhaps I should just drop the matter. How strange
>My voice sounds. Let's leave them alone since
>They wish to be left alone.

JOHNNY: Maybe they're not your parents at all.

HENRY: It's them all right, I know perfectly well it's them
But something's happened to them and for some
reason

> They're pretending not to be them
> Perhaps they've gone crazy. . . .

JOHNNY: Try talking to them in a straightforward manner, Henry.

HENRY: . . . . And I'm unable to speak to them straight-
forwardly, because
There's something very solemn and mysterious about
all this
Exactly as though a mass were being celebrated!
I feel like laughing when I see how solemn I've
become!
My words sound so dignified! I'm simply amused
To see how grave and solemn I've become
But at the very same time I tremble and trembling I
declare
That I tremble — and as a result of this declaration
I tremble even harder and trembling even harder

I again declare that I tremble even harder. . . . But to whom do I
make this declaration? To whom? Someone is listening to me. . . .

> But I don't know who — and as a matter of fact
> I am alone here, all alone, since you are not here
> No! There's no one else here! I am alone
> All alone, completely alone. . . . Oh, weep! Yes, shed
> Tears for me, because I am alone, alone, alone!

JOHNNY: Don't say that. . . . Why do you say such things?

HENRY: Still, if they are my parents the least I could do is go up
to them and say hello. . . .

> Father! Mother!
> Papa! Mamma! It's me, Henry!
> I've come home from the war!

FATHER: (*reluctantly*)
Mother . . . it's Henry!

MOTHER: Henry! Good Heavens!

HENRY: (*with animation*)
Hey, they said something!

MOTHER: Oh, who could have ever foreseen by a divine premonition that something like this . . . oh, my little treasure, my little sunshine, my little sweet pea, oh, how could I have been so blind, and how I used to cry my eyes out for fear I would never see you again, my little sunshine, but here you are, my little sweet pea, my little sparrow, my little treasure, oh, and how you've grown, you're a man now, alleluia, alleluia, come here, let me hug you, my little sweet pea, my little sparrow, my little treasure, my little sunshine, oh, oh, oh. . . .

HENRY: Come, let's hug each other.

MOTHER: Oh, yes, yes, let's hug each other.

FATHER: Well, all right, let's hug each other.

MOTHER: Come, let me hug you.

FATHER: Wait a minute! Not like that.

HENRY: But it's only mamma!

FATHER: Mamma or no mamma, I wouldn't get too close if I were you.

HENRY: But . . . but I am the son.

FATHER: Son or no son, I wouldn't get too close if I were you. . . . Maybe you are the son, but there's no telling what the son has been up to all these years. No sooner does he set foot inside the door and right away he has to be hugged. (*Sharply*) Well, nobody's going to put his arms around me, see, 'cos I'm not an old sack you can just dump in any corner you like!

HENRY: (*to* JOHNNY) They've gone crazy.

JOHNNY: (*to* HENRY) They've gone crazy.

FATHER: And you can cut out all this matey business too, 'cos once you start that the next thing you know is some bastard'll up and pull a fast one on you and then, whaam, right in the kisser . . . or somewhere else for all I know . . . and then pretty soon they'll be trying to take advantage of you, pushing you about and knocking you in the chops, persecuting the hell out of you, hounding and tormenting you, with no regard whatsoever for age or sex, with their bloody, pitiless, spiteful spite. . . .

HENRY: They've gone crazy.

JOHNNY: They've gone crazy.

HENRY: (*unrestrainedly, emphatically, theatrically*)
          It's obvious they couldn't take it
          They've lost their wits
          After all these long and agonizing years
          But such is life. The world nowadays is swarming
          With half-wits. . . .

JOHNNY: (*as above*)
          The world is swarming with half-wits. At least
          Half of all the mothers and fathers in the world
          Have lost their wits because they couldn't endure
          Suffering, affliction and disease
          I know of many such cases myself.

HENRY: So do I!

(*Falls silent, ashamed*) Nevertheless, I must try to make a little conversation with them. (*Loudly, in a conventional tone*) To tell the truth, I didn't recognize you at first.

MOTHER: Neither did we.

HENRY: I didn't recognize you, because . . . well, because I didn't expect. . . . But that doesn't matter. It's not of any real importance. So how have you been getting along?

FATHER: Not bad. What about you?

HENRY: All right, I suppose.

FATHER: Hm. . . .

HENRY: Hm. . . .

Silence.

Well, what'll we do now? We can't just stand here and do nothing. . . .

FATHER: Nothing.

MOTHER: Nothing.

HENRY: Nothing.

JOHNNY: (*unexpectedly*) I could eat something.

MOTHER: But of course! Here we are jabbering away about nothing, oh, but of course, what's the matter with me, of course, one
has to have a bite to eat, certainly, just a minute. . . . I'll have
something ready in less than no time, why of course, this is a day
to celebrate, because our darling Henry has come home, let's see,
we'll find something to eat, just a minute, just a minute. . . .
Here's a table and here are a few chairs. . . . You'll have to settle
for potluck, it isn't what you'd call a feast exactly, but it'll have to
do, I suppose, alleluia, alleluia. . . .

FATHER: That's the spirit, mother, fix us something to eat, but in
a manner which is fitting, with respect . . . as is proper. . . . And
so, in the name of the Father and of the Son, of the Mother and
of the Son, please be seated at our table, my son. . . . But we
can't just sit down at the table in any old way. . . . The table's
over there and we're over here . . . so give me your arm my son,
and you, old girl, let this young gentleman show you to the
table, for such is how it has always been in our family for
centuries and centuries, amen. And now, forward, march!

HENRY: Very well.

They walk two by two.

MOTHER: I still can remember how His Reverence the Pastor
Escorted me to all the festivities at Easter
The table would be laid, the guests all engaged
In the most cheerful conversation!

FATHER: (*thunderously*)
In those days, gentlemen, a man would sit down
To a freshly laid table, and tuck away his pea soup
With such appetite and zest, one would have thought
He were ringing the bells or blowing a trombone!

JOHNNY: How pleasant it is to walk and how pleasant
To exclaim words out loud!

But if we all continue to prate
I'm afraid we shall never get anything to eat!

HENRY: I'm a little confused about this procession of ours.
              I'm not sure
           Whether I am leading father, or he is leading me
           And the form of our meeting strikes me as queer
           But one must adapt oneself to the general atmos-
              phere. . . .

ALL: Yes, each must adapt himself to the general atmos-
              phere!
           Each must adapt himself to the other! Then a concert
              will erupt!

HENRY: How extraordinary!

They sit down at the table.

MOTHER: Forgive us for offering you such a modest meal,
Henry, and you too, Johnny . . . but you see, we do the best we
can under the circumstances. This is a soup made from horse
guts and cat piss.

FATHER: Be quiet, woman! What difference does it make what
it's made from. You've probably noticed, Henry, that you've
found us in a somewhat embarrassing situation in this dumpy,
dumpable dump of a roadside dump — well, you see, that's
because there was a storm, a snowstorm, the roads were closed,
not a soul, thunder and lightning, puddles of water, mud everywhere. . . . Keep your spoon where it is, son, your father hasn't
lifted his spoon to his mouth yet.

HENRY: This tavern . . . it reminds me of something.

FATHER: Never mind about that, forget about it.

MOTHER: There isn't any.

JOHNNY: No.

HENRY: Nothing.

FATHER: It's been transformed.

MOTHER: Distorted.

JOHNNY: Destroyed.

HENRY: Dislocated.

All right, all right, they *have* gone crazy. But they couldn't have gone crazy, because they don't exist and I am only dreaming . . . and the surest sign they don't exist is that I'm able to say they don't exist right in front of them. They only exist in my head. Oh, my head! I've been talking to myself the whole time!

JOHNNY: How's that? What do you mean you've been talking to yourself the whole time?

HENRY: Oh, skip it! (*He begins to eat*)

FATHER: Keep your spoon where it is — your father still hasn't lifted his to his mouth yet.

HENRY: Father, mother — how oppressive all these dreams are — father, mother — as if I didn't have enough problems of my own — father, mother — and all this time I thought they were dead — but not only are they not dead, they are sitting here and. . . .

FATHER: You are a faithful and devoted son, and consequently you will not wish to commence eating before he who has sired you. . . .

HENRY: And I won't go back to my family. I don't have a family any more. I am no longer a son.

FATHER: (*as though he were preaching a sermon*) Gone forever is that love and fidelity which the son has always owed the father, because for centuries and centuries, amen, the father has always been a hallowed and sacrosanct saint, an object of filial devotion under the pain of eternal chastisement. . . .

HENRY: I am a son of the war!

FATHER: And whoever raised a sacrilegious hand against his father would commit a crime so appalling so unnatural, so abominable, so monstrous that afterwards he would pass the rest of his days, from one generation to the next, amid screams and groans of anguish, as one condemned by God and by

Nature, heaped with shame, abandoned, accursed, rejected, forsaken, tormented. . . .

HENRY: The old man's afraid I might belt him. . . .

FATHER: Good soup.

HENRY: (*to* JOHNNY) Think you could beat the daylights out of this father?

JOHNNY: If you could, I could.

FATHER: Pass me the salt.

HENRY: And you wouldn't feel any pangs of conscience after-wards?

JOHNNY: I would if I were alone, but not if there were the two of us, because one would imitate the other.

FATHER: Nothing I like better than stuffing myself with tripe.

HENRY: (*to* JOHNNY) Ha, ha, ha! Well said, Johnny, well said. I agree with what you said just now — ha, ha, ha, yes, yes, I agree with you one hundred per cent. But that's beside the point. (*With growing anxiety*) No, that's completely beside the point. That's not what I had in mind at all. Oh, the hell with it! I'll be damned if I know what's going on around here! All I know is that this is all frightfully oppressive, because every-thing is twisted, understand, bunged up, plugged up, yes, that's it, plugged up . . . and disguised . . . but it seems as if we're not the only ones here . . . I would like to penetrate, elucidate, to solve the riddle. . . . (*He turns the lamp into the centre of the room, revealing* MOLLY, *who is asleep in a chair*) Who is that girl?

MOTHER: Oh, that's the girl who does the service around here.

HENRY: Service?

MOTHER: That's right, a maidservant . . . she serves as a maid. . . Molly, bring us those scraps and that cat cutlet that are lying on the window sill. . . .

The FATHER *scratches himself.*

Are you itching again?

HENRY: By the way, as long as we're going on about nothing in particular. . . . Are any of our friends still alive?

FATHER: A few.

HENRY: Tell me something, I'd be curious to know . . . whatever became of Mary, you remember, the girl I was once engaged to . . . the one who used to come here for the holidays. . . .

FATHER: I don't see any cutlet.

MOTHER: Maybe somebody swiped it.

MOLLY: (*comes closer*) It's not on the window.

MOTHER: Go and look in the reception room, but no dilly-dallying, mind you. . . . Clear the dishes away first.

HENRY: What's your name?

MOLLY: Molly.

FATHER: (*in an ambiguous tone*) Molly.

MOTHER: (*as above*) Molly.

FATHER: She's a servant girl. . . . She serves. . . .

MOTHER: We hired her . . . for everything. . . .

FATHER: She's an all-round servant.

MOTHER: She serves the guests.

FATHER: She serves to render service. . . .
Molly

MOTHER: Molly. . . .

FATHER: Molly. . . .

HENRY: (*to* JOHNNY, *quietly, sadly*) What do you think about all this?

JOHNNY: (*quietly, helplessly*) I don't know. . . . I don't know. . . .

HENRY: (*to* JOHNNY) No, but I know!

JOHNNY: (*to* HENRY) If that's her, why doesn't she speak up? . . . She couldn't have forgotten us. . . . Say something to her, Henry.

HENRY: No.
           How can I speak to her if
           She no longer exists
           She used to exist. . . .
           Oh, what a dirty trick!
           I once had a noble father and mother
           And a fiancée as well, but now it appears
           My father has shut himself up in some inexplicable
               tower
           My mother has become equivocal
           And my fiancée has been swallowed up by a slut
           Bunged, beaten and plugged up by a slut
           And forever imprisoned in a slut. . . .
           Oh, what a dirty trick!
           How vile! How base! How vulgar! But the worst thing
               of all is
           I couldn't give a damn. . . . Hear
           With what ease I say that: I couldn't give a damn.

JOHNNY: (*lightly*) Neither could I.

HENRY: (*lightly*)
           To tell the truth,
           I don't have the faintest idea
           How I should behave:
           The girl I was once engaged to has now become a slut.

JOHNNY: What of it?

HENRY: What of it?
           Exactly — what of it — since
           All of this is just a mere detail.

JOHNNY: A detail!
           Millions of girls
           Have suffered the same fate.

HENRY: Exactly!
           Millions of other people
           Are in the same situation as I.

JOHNNY: The world over!

HENRY: In Warsaw and Peking!

JOHNNY: In Verona and Barcelona!

HENRY: In Paris and in Venice!

JOHNNY: In Liverpool and Istanbul!

MOTHER: In Lyons and in Toulons!

FATHER: In Bucharest and Budapest!

JOHNNY: In Dublin and Berlin!

HENRY: Come on, let's dance!

ALL: (*suddenly*) Let's dance!

HENRY: The son has returned to the house of his parents
               But the house is no longer the house
               And the son is no longer the son. So who
               Has returned and to what?
               Let's forget about the past! Let's march forward!
               May no one return to anything!

   Quiet.

Here is where I sat with her, and once again I'm sitting here.
But what difference does it make? It's all over now. Finished.
There's something else now and there'll be something else
again tomorrow. It's not worth repeating.

   Quiet.

JOHNNY: It's not worth repeating!

HENRY: (*in a romantic tone*)
               Do you see this chair here? That's where I sat with her
               On that memorable night! This is where
               My mother sat and my father over there!
               Exactly as I'm sitting here now. Do you remember?
               That memorable night, our last night together?

MOTHER: Of course I do, my child, of course I remember. . . . I
   sat right over here, and we had sour milk for supper. . . .

FATHER: I sat over here.

JOHNNY: And I sat here . . . here, in this chair, because I remember I was looking out of the window and I said: 'There are flies here.' It all comes back to me now!

HENRY: And I sat over here. . . . (*He sits down*) I was buttering my bread, with her beside me here. . . . I was buttering my bread. (*To* JOHNNY) Why don't you sit down? Sit down. I was buttering my bread.

> And I said: Schearing
> Has inquired about that syringe again.

FATHER: I said something, but I can't remember what.

MOTHER: You don't have a very good memory, but I do. . . . Now what was it you said? Oh, yes! You said, 'My sleeve,' . . . nothing else, just 'my sleeve,' because he'd just got his sleeve caught against the salad dish.

FATHER: That's it! That's it! That's it! I said, 'My sleeve,' on my word of honour! What an extraordinary memory you have!

HENRY: And then I started drumming my fingers on the table and I said: 'I'm getting married in three months.'

MOTHER: That's just what he said, my little sparrow, that's exactly what he said, those are the exact same words he used, that's just how he put it. And then I laid down my cup, chased away another fly and said: 'Henry, what's the matter with you? What's that you're saying? Are you engaged? But isn't that a little. . . .' No, I've got it all wrong. First I said: 'Henry, darling, what are you saying? . . . Pass me the sugar.'

FATHER: That's right, that's right, and then I said 'Let them be happy, mother! Now, now, no need to cry. Bring us something to drink! You're both a little young, but never mind that.' You should have seen her blush! Turned red as a tomato! Well, I never! Ha, ha, ha!

MOTHER: And then she said something.

HENRY: Yes, she said something, but she's gone now.
The wedding fell through. Finished. Nothing.
There she is, hiding in the closet! She refuses to
come out.

Oh, what's the use! I'm surrounded by a void. And
all she does it pout.
Forward! Forward!

ALL: (*except* MOLLY) Forward!

FATHER: The hell with it, dammit!

HENRY: (*to* JOHNNY) How do you like that — a common ordinary maidservant!

JOHNNY: Well, so what if she's a maidservant?

HENRY: That's right, so what if she's a maidservant.

JOHNNY: She's not even bad-looking.

HENRY: You're right, she's not bad-looking, at that.

JOHNNY: Does she sleep here?

HENRY: Does she sleep here?

JOHNNY: (*playfully*) I would like some tea. (*To* MOLLY)
Pssst . . . . Pssst. . . .

FATHER: What's all this pssst-pssst for? There's no need to pssst
around here. If you want something else, all you have to do is
ask me. And don't think you can get away with anything, 'cos
we're not running some dive here, you know. . . . Ohoh, did you
see that? They're already givin' her the eye! Christ Almighty,
it's always the same, night or day, someone's trying to pinch
her, pat her, cuddle her, fondle her, tickle her crotch, and it
always winds up in trouble, trouble, trouble. . . . (*Sharply*)
Don't try to cause any trouble, I'm warning you fellers!

MOTHER: (*in a shrill voice*) Frankie!

FATHER: Don't start anything, I'm warning you!

MOTHER: Calm down, Frankie!

FATHER: Kindly keep your piggish paws off this swinish sow of a
pigged-up pig of a swineherder's pig prick!

MOTHER: Look at him slobber!

FATHER: Pig, pig, pig!

The DRUNKARD *staggers in.*

DRUNKARD: Porky Molly!

FATHER: Get out of here!

DRUNKARD: Hey, Molly, how about a little piece of pork, eh?

FATHER: I'll get it for you myself.

HENRY: (*on the other side, amused*) Porky Molly!

FATHER: (*running up to him*) I'll serve it to him!

DRUNKARD: Hey, Molly, give me some pork!

HENRY: (*obstinately*)
　　　Porky Molly.

DRUNKARD: Give me some pork, Molly!

HENRY: Porky Molly!

FATHER: Oh, for Christ's sake!

DRUNKARD: Pig!

HENRY: (*yelling into space*)
　　　Pig!

JOHNNY: Pig!

MOTHER: (*aside*)
　　　Heaven help us — what a pig!

FATHER: (*to the* DRUNKARD)
　　　Get out of here!

DRUNKARD: A bottle of bitters!

FATHER: (*to* HENRY)
　　　Get out of here!

HENRY: A bottle of bitters!

DRUNKARD: (*louder*)
　　　A bottle of bitters!

HENRY: *(louder)*
         A bottle of bitters!

FATHER: Good God!

DRUNKARD: A bottle of pig bitters!

HENRY: A bottle of pig bitters!

JOHNNY: A bottle of pig bitters!

The DRUNKARDS come in.

DRUNKARDS: Chug, chug, chug!

FATHER: Gentlemen, be reasonable!
         It's almost closing time. Molly, lock the doors!

The DRUNKARDS sit down at the table.

DRUNKARDS: Some stout!
            A pint!
            Some brawn!
            A double shot, straight!
            Molly, some stout! Molly, some kielbasa! Molly,
some   sausage!
            Molly, some brawn!

HENRY: *(aside)*
         Molly, some brawn!

DRUNKARDS: Maxie's an ice-cream man
            Hits the bottle when he can
            Chug, chug, chug!

FATHER: *(to MOLLY)* Hey . . . don't wait on that table!

DRUNKARD: Ah, come on, Molly, come on over here for a
   second, I want to tell you something, Molly me darling. . . .

FATHER: Don't go Molly.

DRUNKARD: Aaah, shut your bloody trap, grandpa. . . . If I feel
   like calling the waitress she's no right to refuse, damn it, and if
   you try and get tough with me, you old duffer, I'll blow myself
   up and blow off your crucifix!

HENRY: *(aside)* Blow off his crucifix!

FATHER: Wait a minute, wait a minute! Okay, okay — Molly, go
and wait on that table!

DRUNKARD: (*looking at him*)
He's got the shits.

DRUNKARDS: (*matter-of-factly*)
He's got the shits.

HENRY: (*aside*)
He's got the shits.

DRUNKARD: Shuuut up. . . .
Close ranks! March!
Forward! Let's go!

A furious march.

DRUNKARDS: Maxie's an ice-cream man
Hits the bottle when he can
Chug, chug, chug!

They stop in front of the FATHER.

DRUNKARD: Shut your traaap . . . you pig. . . .
Pig!
He's got the shits. . . .
That's what's the matter, he's got a bad case of the
shits
He's gone and dirtied his pants!

2nd DRUNKARD: (*gloomily*)
He's got the shits.

3rd DRUNKARD:
Has he ever. . . .

DRUNKARD: And seeing as how I've scared the shit out of him,
I'm going to let him have it. Isn't that so, Miss Molly?

DRUNKARDS: Well, let 'im have it then! Let 'im have it!

DRUNKARD: I'm going to let 'im have it!

DRUNKARDS: Well, let 'im have it then! Let 'im have it!

DRUNKARD: I'm going to let 'im have it!

HENRY: Well, let 'im have it!

DRUNKARD: I'm going to let 'im have it!

MOTHER: (*in a shrill voice*) Frankie, they're going to let you have it!

DRUNKARDS: All right, boys, let's let 'im have it!

DRUNKARD: All right, let's let 'im have it!

They advance towards the FATHER.

DRUNKARDS: All right, let 'im have it!

DRUNKARD: I'm going to let 'im have it!

Silence.

>   I'd let him have it, but the bastardly bastard has a
>   kisser like a rock. . . .
>   It won't budge. . . . And if it won't budge, then. . . .
>   (*To* MOLLY) Molly!
>   There's a lot of room on the floor!

DRUNKARDS: (*sullenly*) It won't budge. . . . (*To* MOLLY)
Molly. . . .

DRUNKARD: And that's not all. . . . Look how quiet it's become. . . .

HENRY: (*to himself, aloud*) It's true. It has become quiet in
here. . . .

DRUNKARD: Chug, chug, chug!

A furious march.

DRUNKARDS: Maxie's an ice-cream man
                He hits the bottle when he can
                Chug, chug, chug!

            Well, let 'im have it!

DRUNKARD: Okay, I'm going to let 'im have it!

HENRY: (*to himself*) How much longer can this go on?

DRUNKARD: (*aside, in a different tone*) Not much longer now.

HENRY: (*to the* DRUNKARD) What's outside the window?

DRUNKARD: (*as above*) Fields — as far as the eye can see.

The DRUNKARDS *approach the* FATHER.

But first of all I'm going to smash this guy right in the kisser and then I'm going to stamp all over him, flatten him, squish out his guts and spit all over him 'cos I'm not afraid — Molly. . . .

> But he's got a mug like a rock!
> And if it won't budge, there's not a damn thing I

can   do. . . .
> But what a mug he's got, what a mug!

2nd DRUNKARD:
> A mug like a house!

3rd DRUNKARD:
> A mug like a priest!

Silence.

4th DRUNKARD: (*suddenly*) Hey, he's got a fly on his nose!

DRUNKARD: So what?

4th DRUNKARD: Well, why don't you knock it off for him? You're not going to just let it sit there, are you? Isn't that right, Miss Molly?

DRUNKARD: Bloodybloodybloody fly, bloodybloodybloody fly, bloodybloodybloody fly. . . . (*He raises his hand*)

FATHER: (*very softly*) Don't you dare. . . .

HENRY: (*aside, dramatically*) Oh, oh, he said something!

FATHER: (*softly*)
> Don't you dare, I won't tolerate it
> I won't tolerate it
> I won't stand for it
> I won't stand for it, because I won't stand for it
> I can't stand it!
> And if I can't stand it, then . . . then. . . .
> Then I don't know what. . . .

DRUNKARD: (*confidentially*)
>I'm going to let 'im have it, Molly, I'm going to let 'im have it!

DRUNKARDS: (*confidentially*)
>Well, let 'im have it then, let 'im have it!

FATHER: (*shouting*)
>You pigs!
>Keep away from me, or you'll be sorry
>If anybody touches me, something awful
>I repeat: something awful
>So awful that . . . that I don't know what.
>There'll be weeping and screaming and the gnash
>   ing of teeth,
>The rack and execution, hell and execration,
>A levelling, piercing, pulverizing squeal
>That'll blow this whole universe to kingdom come
>   . . . . Indeed! Indeed!
>
>Because no one, because no one may touch me
>Because no one, because no, be-be-because
>I'm untouchable, I'm untouchable, I'm untouchable
>Because I'll curse the lot of you!

DRUNKARDS: Tut, tut, tut! A king, a king, an untouchable king!

DRUNKARD: Get a load of him! He's a king!
>Just for that I'm going to touch him with this finger!
>Isn't that right, Miss Molly?

FATHER: (*fleeing*) Keep away from me, or I'll curse you!

HENRY: (*suddenly*) Stop! Stay where you are!

The stage becomes motionless.

I really don't know how I ought to behave. . . . (*To* JOHNNY)
Johnny! But I suppose I shall have to behave somehow or
other. . . . (*With regret*) Forgive me for speaking in an artificial
manner, but everything here is artificial!

JOHNNY: (*briskly, defiantly*)
>Don't worry about it!

What do you care if something is artificial
As long as you yourself are natural!

HENRY: That's right, I am natural, I would like to be natural
I don't want to be solemn! But how can I help
Not being solemn when my voice sounds solemn?

Silence.

What a terrifying silence.
It's so quiet my ears are ringing
And how strange, how awfully
Strange that I am speaking
But if I were silent
My silence would likewise seem strange
What am I to do?
Suppose I sat down
In this chair here
(*He sits down*)
   and started
Cracking jokes, laughing, or moving
My hands and feet. . . . No, it's no use! Even
The artlessness of these gestures is artificial
And they are transformed into some sort of spell. . . .

Suppose I put my feet up on this table, tossed back my head, lit a cigarette and said: What business is it of mine whether they beat up my father or rape my ex-fiancée?. . . What's the sense of blowing everything out of proportion?

Let's not exaggerate!

What's one more or less. . . . Can't he stand it? But I can stand it that he can't stand it. . . . Father, father. . . .

What kind of a father is he anyway? He's an ordi
   nary father
The most ordinary kind of father. . . . We are all
The most ordinary kind of people. . . . Suppose I say
All this and even more. Very well. I said it
But this again
Sounds solemn, and transforms what I am saying
   into a

DECLARATION
And it sinks like a stone
Into that silence. . . Aha! Now I know why
I do not speak but declare. Because you are not here
And I am alone, alone, alone. I am not speaking
To anyone and therefore I must be artificial
Because if I am not speaking to anyone and yet I
    speak just the same
Then I must be artificial.

What'll I do? Sit down? No. Go for a walk? That doesn't make any sense either. But I can't go on behaving as though I had nothing to do with all this. What's a person supposed to do in such a situation? I might kneel down, that's true, I might kneel down. . . . Of course that would be pretty . . . but I did say I might kneel down . . . even though it would look a little . . . but I did say I might kneel down. . . .

He kneels down a little on one side.

Well, what do you know! I knelt down. But I knelt down quietly and not for myself, but for them, and not for them, but for myself as though I were a priest . . . a priest . . . of what I don't know. . . .

FATHER: *(abruptly, aside)* Of what I don't know.

MOTHER: Nobody knows.

DRUNKARD: There's nobody here.

JOHNNY: Nobody, nothing.

HENRY: It doesn't matter!
    I am kneeling here before him! And now try
    To dismiss my genuflection, now try to
    Ignore my genuflection, now try to make it
    Disappear! *(To the DRUNKARD)* Go on, hit him!
    I kneel down before him!

2nd DRUNKARD: The King!

MOTHER: The King!

DRUNKARD: The King!

DRUNKARDS: The King! The King!

HENRY: What do you mean, the King?

DRUNKARDS: (*completely drunk*)
            The King, the King, the King!

Their cries become more and more accelerated in tempo. The DIGNITARIES *come in.*

FATHER: Henry!
            Oh, oh, Henry!

MOTHER: Oh, Henry!

DIGNITARIES: Henry!

HENRY: Oh, Henry! (*Stands up*)

FATHER: Thank you, my son, I accept the homage which you
                            have rendered me
            I accept it and once again I accept it
            And I cannot accept it enough. . . .
            (*With sincerity*) Long have I thirsted after honours.

HENRY: What kind of a masquerade is this?

Quiet.

FATHER: (*with difficulty, vehemently*)
            Dignitaries!

DIGNITARIES: The King! The King!

FATHER: Dignitaries of my Person!

DIGNITARIES: The King! The King!

FATHER: Dignitaries of my dignity! Bid welcome to the Prince
            Bow down before him in humble obeisance,
            Prince Henry, my son, who from a far-off war
            Has come.

HENRY: What kind of rubbish is this?

FATHER: (*gravely, sclerotically*)
            Help! Help!

Oh, sweet Jesus of Nazareth! Oh, Mary most holy! Oh, Jesus,
my Jesus! Help me! But it was he, my son, my seed, my
offspring most holy who only a moment ago delivered me from

This sow of a souse who, in his drunken stupor,
Blindly, brazenly, with extreme wantonness,
Rushed at me and with
His
Piggish
Finger

My untouchable person tried to touch! My person! My person!
My untouch. . . . Nobody may touch . . . because it's forbid-
den. . . . Prohibited. Nobody!

DIGNITARIES: Oh, sweet Jesus!

FATHER: He won't try to touch me any more!
Nor inflate himself to deflate my person
Nor squish, nor stamp, nor spit on me!
Because Henry, Henry, Henry! Oh, Henry!

MOTHER: (*triumphantly*)
Henry!

DIGNITARIES: Oh, Henry!

HENRY: Oh, Henry!
This is getting sillier by the minute!

FATHER: Kneel down
Kneel down, Henry.

HENRY: What for?

MOTHER: (*in a shrill voice*) Kneel down, Henry!

FATHER: Kneel down, kneel down! I'll kneel down too
Kneel down! Let everyone kneel. . . . (*He kneels*)

The DIGNITARIES *kneel down.*

HENRY: I'm not going to stand here by myself. . . . (*He gazes
around with distrust and kneels down*) I wish to hell I knew
what was going on. (*He notices that he and his* FATHER *are
kneeling opposite one another*) I am kneeling before him and
he is kneeling before me. This is a farce! What an old copycat
he is! (*With increasing rage*) How disgusting!

FATHER   Wait a minute! I'm kneeling in the wrong direction.

(*Kneels down with his back to* HENRY) I kneel down before the Lord! I address myself to the Lord! I commend myself to Almighty God, to the Holy Trinity, to His inexhaustible goodness, to His mercy most holy, His protection most sublime. . . . Oh, Henry, Henry!. . . In Him is there shelter, in Him is there comfort, in Him is our refuge. . . .

> My Father
> Thy son am I
> Thou art my Father. . . .

HENRY: He's praying.

FATHER: Thou art my king!

HENRY: I can't get up now — it wouldn't be proper.

FATHER: Oh, my Father, Oh, my King, to Thee I do solemnly
>>> swear
> Love
> Honour
> Respect

HENRY: He's swearing to God, but it's as if *I* were swearing to *him*. (*Aloud*) I've had about all I can take of this. (*Stands up*)

FATHER: Henry, Henry. . . . My Father, I stand beside Thee, I am Thy servant. I shall not forsake Thee, my Father, and in return Thou shalt. . . . Thou shalt return my beloved to me, my sweetheart, amen, amen, amen. . . so that everything may be done in a respectable manner, as is fitting. . . .

HENRY: Hey, what is this? Is he whispering to God or to me?

FATHER: Thou shalt return my betrothed to me!

HENRY: He will return my betrothed to me?

FATHER: Thou shalt grant me a marriage!

HENRY: He will grant me a marriage?

FATHER: Thou shalt grant me a respectable marriage . . . a proper marriage as has always been the custom in our family. . . As it was in former times! Let everything be as it used to be! Thou shalt grant me a marriage to this chaste and immaculate virgin, my fiancée, my sweetheart . . . a respectable marriage. . . .

Everyone slowly rises.

HENRY: A marriage?

FATHER: A marriage.

MOTHER: A marriage.

HENRY: A marriage?

FATHER: A marriage.

MOLLY: A marriage.

A DIGNITARY: A marriage.

MOTHER: A marriage.

A DIGNITARY: A marriage.

HENRY: A marriage?

The FATHER *and* MOTHER *smile at him indulgently, with delight, with emotion.*

FATHER: In the name of the Father
            And of the Son! Do you see
            This young lady here who in appearance
            Is nothing but an ordinary maidservant?
            The maidservant of some dumpy dump?

DIGNITARIES: We see her, Sire.

FATHER: *(emphatically, insistently)*
            This girl is neither a whore
            Nor a maidservant! She is a noble,
            Modest, untouchable young lady who has been
            Ravished, enslaved, tortured, plugged up,
            Abused and spat upon by these good-for-nothing
                bums. . . .
            In defiance of all laws, human and divine. . . . Damn
                you pigs!
            This girl is not a pig! Have
            A little heart, you people! A little understanding!
            Have a little pity! Therefore I do declare
            And I decree, I command with all my might, I

declare once and for all,
To all those present
That I restore her former dignity
And command that she be honoured
As though she were myself or the Most Holy
Virgin in her untouchable honour, in the name
Of the Father and of the Son!

HENRY: (*to* JOHNNY) This is nothing but a dream, it's only a dream . . . a little naive maybe, but what do I care.

JOHNNY: That's right! What do you care whether or not it's a dream . . . as long as it gives you pleasure.

HENRY: Pleasure.

Meanwhile, the FATHER, MOTHER, MOLLY *and the* DIGNITARIES *gather around him.*

MOTHER: Oh, look how he's blushing!

FATHER: Ha, ha, ha! He's ashamed. . . . Now, now, Henry, look at me, look at me. . . .

HENRY: What for?

FATHER: Because tomorrow's the wedding. . . .

HENRY: But I don't understand. . . .

FATHER: (*aside*) Tssst. . . . Surely you're not going to fool around with some cheap tuppenny ha'penny whore, not when you have the chance to marry a respectable young lady. . . . In our family it has always been the custom to have a respectable marriage. Your mother and I were married in a proper manner, and it is only fitting that you do the same. . . . You'll see everything will turn out all right. . . . (*In a loud voice*) Thank you, my son, for showing me your affection. . . . Soon we shall be celebrating your marriage and with it my joy and that of your mother, my spouse, and as for that which is already past, squandered and forgotten, we simply won't talk about that any more, as far as we're concerned it never happened, it no longer is, it isn't. . . .

MOTHER: (*in a very loud voice*) Alleluia!

Music, wedding march. FATHER *and* MOTHER, HENRY *and*
MOLLY, JOHNNY *and the* DIGNITARIES *march around the stage
in a solemn and cordial procession.*

HENRY: (*in a very loud voice*)
              Is it possible to imagine anything more improbable
              Than this farcical march of phantoms in a fog of
                 illusion?
              And yet does it fill my breast with glee and cause
my   poor heart to sing
              When me to my former lover this festive march
does   bring.
              (*To everyone*) Forgive me, I am a rhymester.

MOTHER: It's such times as these that gladden a mother's
              heart,
              Which for so many years has stood in disregard!

FATHER: The music is playing, the couples in procession
              As once was the custom in times gone by!
              Follow me, gentlemen! As God is our Protector!
              Don't stop, gentlemen! Come on!
              March forward! Forward! Come on, let's go!
              Faster, faster! Keep in step!
              Step lively, gentlemen! March in style!
              Don't fall behind! March forward!
              Forward! Forward! Come on, let's go!
              (*He notices the* DRUNKARD)
              Stop, stop, stop! He's come here to gawp at us!
              Seize this man, arrest him and throw him into
              Some dark and dreary, foul and fetid, godforsaken
                 dungeon!
              (*To the* DRUNKARD) I'm going to let you have it, see!

DRUNKARD: I'm going to let you have it, see!

FATHER: You?
              Me?

DRUNKARD: I'll touch you yet. . . .
              (*To* MOLLY) Isn't that right, Miss Molly?

FATHER: You pig!

DRUNKARD: You pig!

FATHER: You pig!

ACT TWO

A large room, in semi-darkness.

HENRY: (*leaning up against a column*)
        O to divine
        The sense of this dream. . . .

Two by two the DIGNITARIES *pass by in the penumbra and mount the stairs to an elevated platform which fades away in the darkness.*

1st DIGNITARY:
        A maidservant who served to render service!

2nd DIGNITARY:
        And the king of the tavern is a tangible tavern-keeper!

They pass by.

3rd DIGNITARY:
        The wedding will take place shortly.

4th DIGNITARY:
        The wedding? That's a joke!

They pass by.

5th DIGNITARY: How much longer must we go on making asses of ourselves, poking our noses into this servant girl's business?

6th DIGNITARY: And that drunkard has broken loose from his shackles and is roaming about the neighbourhood.

They pass by. The FATHER *approaches.*

HENRY: Father!

FATHER: Yes, it's me, Henry. . . . They're getting ready for the marriage. In a minute we're going to give you a wedding that'll make everybody green with envy. . . . (*Pointing into the darkness*) They're making preparations over there now. Just keep a firm grip on yourself!

HENRY: What kind of a marriage? Who will perform the ceremony, where and how?

FATHER: Who? The Bishop. I've sent for the Bishop to make sure everything goes the way it should. Don't worry. I've taken care of everything, but don't lose your head, Henry, don't lose your head . . . and for God's sake don't do anything stupid — otherwise the marriage will be a flop. . . . Remember, it's not just your father who's involved here — there's your sweetheart to consider too. . . .

HENRY: (*into space*) Sometimes I think this is all very wise, and other times. . . .

FATHER: Tsst. . . . But whatever you do, Henry, don't betray me, because there are enough traitors around here already. . . . Don't try to make a laughingstock out of me, Henry, I beg of you . . . because the place is crawling with traitors . . . traitors . . . traitors. . . . Traitors! (*He withdraws, then climbs up to the platform*)

HENRY: I don't know what my feelings are!

Light. FATHER *appears on the platform surrounded by a* COUNCIL AND COURT. *The faces of the* DIGNITARIES *are expressive to the point of caricature, wise, slightly contemptuous; the costumes are magnificant but border on the burlesque.*

What majesty! (*He goes before the throne*)
Here I am!

FATHER: Henry!

COUNCIL AND COURT: Oh, Henry!

HENRY: Oh, Henry!

FATHER: Henry, my son, we are about to embark
Upon your nuptial ceremony. Soon
Will the bridal party usher in the maid

> With whom you'll be united world without end
> Amen, amen.

MOTHER: (*fervently*)
> Amen.

CHANCELLOR: (*wisely and venerably*)
> Amen.
> That was a grave and lofty speech.

DIGNITARY/TRAITOR: (*aside*)
> Amen.
> That was an asinine and ridiculous speech.

FATHER: (*as though frightened*)
> I say

It will take place immediately. In a moment. Because it must take place, I decreed it, I proclaimed it. . . . And if anybody tries to stand in the way!. . . Out, out, you filthy maggots, out, out, you good-for-nothing bums!

> Oh, oh, gentlemen of my council! A short while ago
> A pack of these slimy, rotten, low-down,
> Stinking, slobbering, soused-up sows
> Attacked me and tried to touch
> My person!

COUNCIL AND COURT:
> Oh, my God!

FATHER: Even though I am the King!

COUNCIL AND COURT:
> Oh, my God!

FATHER: Even though I am untouchable!

COUNCIL AND COURT:
> For heaven's sake!

FATHER: (*heavily, sclerotically*) Oh, woe, woe! What a terrible sacrilege, what an intolerable, unthinkable, unpardonable blasphemy! And that's not all. I hear that sow of a souse has broken loose from his shackles while his guards were out getting pickled. . . Chancellor of my Council, command that the gates be closed and have the guards put on alert — there's no telling what these drunks will do. I have an itch. Command that the gates be closed!

DIGNITARY/TRAITOR: (*unexpectedly, brazenly*)
     Ha, ha, ha! That's impossible!
     Ha, ha, ha!

TRAITORS: Ha, ha, ha!

FATHER: What do you mean?

DIGNITARY/TRAITOR: Forgive me, Your Majesty, forgive me, Your Majesty, but His Majesty can't just close his gates to any old drunk who happens to come along, since that would mean His Majesty is afraid of any old drunk and that would be unthinkable because that would constitute an affront to His Majesty, and His Majesty cannot commit an affront to the majesty of His Majesty. . . .

TRAITORS: Well said!

FATHER: What, what, what?

I only mentioned it because that drunken swine has been getting more aggressive lately . . . but if it's impossible, then it's impossible. Don't stretch your luck, you pigs! I know what you've got up your sleeves!

     I have no need of such measures
     Because this ceremony will be so ceremonious
     So dignified, so respectable and so majestic
     In all its majestical majesty, that
     No scum on earth would have the nerve to. . . .
          (*Intoxicated*) Sound the trumpets
     Because the son for the greater glory of his father
     Is about to enter the marital state
     By virtue of my royal decree, yes
     By my most sovereign decree
     Now on with it, on with it!
     Come on, let's go!

COUNCIL AND COURT: (*standing up with fury*)
>   On with it! On with it!
>   Come on, let's go!

FATHER: Stop, stop, everything must be arranged beforehand, so everything goes the way it should. . . . I have an itch. Chancellor of my Council, scratch me. Where is the ceremonial cloak? Put the ceremonial cloak and grand-ducal hat on my son and gird him with the sacred sword!

2nd DIGNITARY: Amen.

3rd DIGNITARY: That was wise.

DIGNITARY/TRAITOR: (*aside*) That was silly as a goose!

2nd DIGNITARY: Our noble young man will look powerful and magnificent in these vestments.

DIGNITARY/TRAITOR: Comical and idiotic, but that's his affair.

Pause.

HENRY: Do I really have to put all that on? (JOHNNY *hands him the vestments*) Oh, is that you, Johnny?

JOHNNY: It's me.

HENRY: Who are you, that is to say, what are you?

JOHNNY: (*clumsily, as though embarrassed*) I've been assigned to your service, Your . . . . Your Highness. . . .

HENRY: I can't talk to you. I feel awkward. . . . Hand me my hat. I look funny, eh?

JOHNNY: Yes and no.

HENRY: Now gird me with the sacred sword. This is a joke, but it doesn't matter. The main thing is I'm going to marry her. (*Suddenly this dialogue becomes public, as though both had forgotten about the presence of the* KING *and* COURT)

JOHNNY: Of course it doesn't matter
>   The main thing is you're going to marry her.

HENRY: I have to adapt myself to the circumstances, but

don't think for a moment
That I take any of this nonsense seriously.
I do it more out of curiosity, I'm anxious to see
What the outcome will be, besides what harm can it
     do me
To amuse myself. . . .

JOHNNY: That's the spirit
            It's better to amuse yourself
            Than to be bored. . . .

HENRY: That's it exactly!

   HENRY *turns to the* KING *in his ceremonial attire; laughter of
   the* TRAITORS; *derisory names are flung down at him.*

1st TRAITOR: Clown!

2nd TRAITOR: Buffoon!

3rd TRAITOR: Imbecile!

FATHER: (*in a vulgar manner*)
                Aaaah, shuut up!
                Keep your bloody traps shut!
                I didn't give anyone permission to speak!
                I give the floor to my son
                Let him speak. (*Panic-stricken*) Henreee, say some-
                                                   thing!

HENRY: What'll I say?

FATHER: (*in absolute terror*) Henree, say something, but for the
   love of God, say something clever . . . say something clever!
   Shuut up, pigs! Now you're going to see how my son can
   talk . . . he'll put you in your places, he'll teach you a thing or
   two. Come on, Henreee, say something, but something clever,
   say something clever, because if you don't then . . . then. . . .

HENRY: Then what?

FATHER: That's just what they're waiting for!

   General expectation.

DIGNITARY/TRAITOR: He will speak foolishly, because he looks
  foolish.

2nd DIGNITARY: He will speak cleverly, because he looks clever.

General expectation.

HENRY: Honestly
             I don't know what to say, but I shall soon find out
             What I will have said.

1st GROUP: What a brilliant idea!

2nd GROUP: What an idiotic idea!

HENRY: (*musingly*)
             I am foolish
             And yet I am to speak cleverly. . . .

ALL: Here comes a confession. . . .

HENRY: (*with sincerity*)
             Again do my words
             Acquire extraordinary power, while I stand here by
                                   myself
             And speak to you alone. But what should I say?

  (*To himself*) If I say something wise, it will sound foolish,
  because I am foolish. And if I say something foolish. . . .

FATHER: No, no, Henreee!

HENRY: (*to himself*) If I'm unable to uphold the grandeur of this
  majesty, this majesty will sink to the level of my buffoonery. I
  can't think of anything clever to say — just the same old empty
  thoughts and words. . . . Wait a minute! Now I know what I will
  say.

             (*To everyone*) My words are vapid
             But they reverberate off you
             And become magnified by your majesty —
             Not by the majesty of the one who speaks
             But by the majesty of the one who listens.

1st GROUP: Well spoken!
             Wisely spoken!

HENRY: I am talking nonsense
                But you are listening wisely to me, and hence
                I am becoming wise.

COUNCIL AND COURT: Wisdom! Wisdom!

MOTHER: What a mind he has, eh?

HENRY: I have no dignity
                I lost my dignity a long time ago. But my father
                Has elevated me to a new dignity now. And so I'm
                                    becoming
                Wiser and more dignified than I am. And I accept it,
                Yes, I accept it. I do hereby proclaim
                That I wish to be married in a manner sublime.
                So let's get on with it! Where is she?
                Show her in and forward, forward!

COUNCIL AND COURT: (*standing up, with fury*)
                Wisdom! Dignity! Marriage! On with it!
                Forward, forward, forward!

FATHER: (*thunderously*) With wisdom profound and dignity
    sublime has my son expounded. Open the gates and bring in
    the bride and His Holiness the Bishop, and let the trumpets
    trumpet with all their might into the very heart of nature; let the
    trumpets trumpet, I say, so as to terrify and terrorize any pig
    who's piggish enough to pig up the works, because there's no
    dearth of these dirty pigs and . . . aaah, the pigggs, the pigggs,
    the piggggggs. . . .

Trumpets. MOLLY, *dressed in a sumptuous gown, comes in
together with the* BRIDAL PARTY; *through another door enters*
BISHOP PANDULF *followed by his retinue.*

FATHER: Henreee!

COUNCIL AND COURT: Oh, Henry!

HENRY: Oh, Henry!

FATHER: (*in a choked voice, as though frightened*) We are about
    to begin. . . . In our family it has always been the custom to
    have a respectable marriage. Don't cry, mother. (*To* MOLLY *and*

HENRY) All right, both of you stand over here . . . bow your heads. . . . (*Aloud*) We are about to embark upon the most holy act of matrimony, in the name of the Father and of the Son. . . (*Aside*) Kneel down and let the trumpets trumpet. . . . Let the bridesmaids take the train in their hands. . . . Chancellor, hand me my sceptre . . . put on my crown. . . . (*Aloud*) In the name of the Father and of the Son. (*Aside*) And now His Holiness the Bishop will bind their hands with the holy sash as proof of this

> Crushing, shattering,
> Omnipotent act performed
> In the presence of our majesty! Sound the trumpets!
> Hand us the holy sash! Down on your knees!
> Oh, Lord! Help! My good people!
> So be it! And so it shall be! Such is my decree!
> Such is my will!

DIGNITARY/TRAITOR: (*loudly, insolently*) Treason!

The DRUNKARD *staggers in.*

FATHER: (*stupidly*) Heyyy . . . what's going on here?

A long silence.

DRUNKARD: I beg your pardon. . . . It's nothing. . . . I was just. . . .

FATHER: (*terrified*) Ask this man who gave him permission to come in here and have him removed at once.

DRUNKARD: A bottle of vodka, a fifth, some gin, four bottles of beer and a herring sandwich!

A VOICE: He's drunk. . . .

2nd VOICE: To the gills. . . .

General laughter, sighs of relief.

HENRY: I do not know this man, and yet
            I have the feeling I do know him. . . .
            (*With solemn meekness*)
            But in any case
            I cannot help knowing
            Everything which is happening here. . . .

FATHER: He's drunk. . . .
            Throw him out, take him away, show him the door. . . .

CHANCELLOR: (*approaches the* DRUNKARD) What are you doing
here, my good man? Do you not realize that you are standing in
the presence of His Royal Majesty?

DRUNKARD: Ai-yai-yai. . . . His Majesty the King! Good heavens!

FATHER: All right, all right, that'll do,
            You are in luck, my good fellow, you have seen the
                                    King
            Now go on home and sleep it off.
            Oh, how distressing is this disease of drink
            That brings our people closer to the brink!

COURT: Oh, indeed! Indeed!

CHANCELLOR: Here, buy yourself a drink, now buzz off!. . . Why
don't you go away?

*The following utterances should be pronounced with an air of
perfunctoriness, apathy.*

DIGNITARY/TRAITOR: Why don't you go away?

DRUNKARD: Because I can't.

2nd DIGNITARY: You can't?

DRUNKARD: I can't.

3rd DIGNITARY: And why can't you?

DRUNKARD: Because I feel funny.

CHANCELLOR: (*to the* FATHER)
            The poor fellow's embarrassed, he can't move
            He doesn't know how to behave, ha, ha, ha!

FATHER: Ha, ha, ha!

CHANCELLOR:
            Ha, ha, ha!
            (*Indicating the door with his finger*)
            Beat it, I tell you!

DRUNKARD: (*with awe*)
          A finger!

CHANCELLOR:
          Beat it!

DRUNKARD: A finger!

CHANCELLOR:
          Out!

DRUNKARD: What a finger!

COURT: Ha, ha, ha, a finger, a finger!

DRUNKARD: (*examining his finger*) It's not like mine. . . . Mine is vulgar, grubby-looking . . . a domestic finger, a peasant's finger . . . just right for nose-picking.

Laughter

A coarse finger, the finger of a village clod . . . why it's an insult even to display such a finger before such august personages. . . .

CHANCELLOR: Get out of here!

DRUNKARD: Okay, okay, I'm going, but I can't because everyone's staring at my finger.

DIGNITARY/TRAITOR: Why don't you stick it in your pocket?

VOICES: Stick it in your ear!
          Or stick it in your eye!

DRUNKARD: I'd like to put it away, but I can't because everyone's looking at it! If I so much as point at something with this finger (*inadvertently points at* HENRY) then right away everybody looks to see what it is I'm pointing at.

HENRY: (*softly*)
          Pig. . . .

DRUNKARD: (*softly*)
          Pig. . . .

(*Aloud*) They're gawping at my finger as if it were somehow extraordinary! And the more they look, the more extraordinary it becomes, and the more extraordinary it becomes, the more they look and the more they look, the more extraordinary it becomes, and the more extraordinary it becomes, the more they look, and the more they look, the more Extraordinary it becomes. . . .

> This is an extraordinary finger!
> This is a powerful Finger!
> Oh, how they've pumped up my finger!

And if I now decided to. . .to toushhh someone with this finger. . . .

FATHER: Shut up!

DRUNKARD: — even though that person is untoushhable. . . .

FATHER: Shut up!

DRUNKARD: (*brutally*) And once I toushh, I get cocky!

TRAITORS: Go ahead! On with it! On with it!

FATHER: (*shouting*) Pig!

DRUNKARD: (*shouting*) Pig!

FATHER: (*in a very calm voice*)
> Friends, gentlemen of my Council and personages
> Of my person. . . .
> (*He bursts out*) Hold on to me, I'm exploding!
> (*Frightened by his own outburst*) I'm bursting. . . .
>   I'm exploding. . . .
> I'm bursting out in such horrifying,
> Terrifying anger, that . . . oh . . . oh . . . oh. . . .
> (*Feebly*) I feel weak. . . .

MOTHER: Frankie! he feels weak!

COURT: The King feels weak! The King is sick!

FATHER: (*feebly, imploringly*)
> Henreee. . . .

COUNCIL AND COURT: (*powerfully*)
> Oh, Henry!

HENRY: Oh, Henry!

    Henry, in the name of the Father, in the name of the
      Son
    In the name of the Father and of the Son!

HENRY *approaches the* DRUNKARD *whose finger has been dominating the scene.*

    You pig!

DRUNKARD: You pig!

HENRY: (*calmly*)
    You pig!
    Put that finger away!

DRUNKARD: (*drunk*) I don't know what you're talking about!

HENRY: Put it away, or else I'll put it away for you!

DRUNKARD: A bottle of booze!

HENRY: Put it away or I'll pounce on it and put it away myself. . . .I'll pounce on it. . . . (*A moment later*) Look how idiotically it sticks out . . . right in the middle of everything. . . . No, I can't pounce on it . . . because the whole thing is preposterous . . . it's too silly for words. . . .

TRAITORS: (*sharply*)
    Silly!
    Silly as a goose!

HENRY: Stop, stop! I'm not silly — it's that finger which is silly! He stuck it out on purpose so as to make a mockery of everything — to make me out to be a lunatic!

DRUNKARD: (*pointing at* HENRY) Lunatic!

TRAITORS: Lunatic!

HENRY: Be careful, I'm warning you. . . . Don't exasperate me, or I shall wake up . . . and you will all disappear. . . . (*To* MOLLY) You will disappear too. . . .

Silence. The stage becomes motionless.

    But perhaps
    This is not a dream, perhaps I really have gone crazy

Perhaps I'm not here at all, but in reality I'm lying in some hospital, and while feverishly thrashing about, I only imagine that I am here. . . . Who knows what might have happened to me?

> Perhaps my brain has been damaged by a bullet?
> Or by an explosion?
> Perhaps I've been taken captive and tortured, or
>   perhaps
> I fell on something, or something fell on me
> Perhaps I became bored . . . and was no longer able. . . .

Or perhaps they ordered me — despatched me — forced me to do something which I couldn't bear. No, there is not a single thing which might not have happened to me — everything and even more than everything is possible. But suppose I am not in a hospital and nothing abnormal has happened to me. All right . . . and yet. . . . Oh, how many insanities have I taken part in?

> Ohhh. . . .
> Even though I was the most healthy . . . the most
>   rational
> The most balanced person
> Others forced me to commit
> Atrocious acts, murderous acts,
> Insane, moronic, and yes, licentious acts. . . .

This raises a simple question: If in the course of several years a person fulfils the function of a madman, is he not then really a madman? And what does it matter that I am healthy if my actions are sick — eh Johnny? But those who forced me to commit these insanities were also healthy

> And sensible
> And balanced. . . . Friends, companions, brothers —
>   so much
> Health
> And such sick behaviour? So much sanity
> And yet so much madness? So much humanity

And yet so much inhumanity? And what does it matter if taken separately each of us is lucid, sensible, balanced, when alto-gether we are nothing but a gigantic madman who furiously

Writhes about, screams, bellows and blindly
Rushes forward, overstepping his own bounds
Ripping himself out of himself. . . . Our madness
Is outside ourselves, out there. . . . There, there, out
    there.
Where I myself end, there begins
My wantonness. . . . And even though I live in peace
Within myself, still do I wander outside myself
And in dark, wild spaces and nocturnal places
Surrender myself to some unbounded chaos!

CHANCELLOR: This is a funeral march!

FATHER: This is a funeral march!

HENRY: That's it, a funeral march!
Once again they have spoken. And I have spoken,
And this finger is jutting out in the middle like the
    finger of a lunatic
And here I am talking to myself and gesticulating in
    absolute solitude like a lunatic. . . .

DRUNKARD: Lunatic!

TRAITORS: Lunatic!

They advance toward HENRY.

HENRY: Stay where you are! I am here at the King's behest.

DRUNKARD: The King is a lunatic!

HENRY: Stop!

Suppose my father has gone mad, but in his madness he is still
a defender of virtue and dignity — in which case he can't be
mad! Yes, that's the truth, that's the most truthful truth — and
hence that solemnity, wisdom, and gravity which have de-
scended upon me. Look how wisely I am standing! My wisdom
and my dignity are invincible!
And he just stands there with his finger like an imbecile!
Go ahead — I dare you to touch me!

FATHER: Henry!

COUNCIL AND COURT:
          Oh, Henry!

HENRY: Oh, Henry!. . .
            Throw that drunkard out of here!

The DIGNITARIES *advance toward the* DRUNKARD.

DRUNKARD: (*slowly, putting his finger away*) Hey, not so rough,
eh? . . . I'm an intelligent person too. . . . (*He suddenly becomes exceedingly clever. To* HENRY)

                        I'm not half
                        As dumb as you think. . . .

(*A moment later*) What d'you say you and I have a little talk on
the side, eh? You know — one wise man to another. . . .

HENRY: (*startled*) What about?

DRUNKARD: We'll see. We'll have a wise little chat. . . . (*To
everyone*) Because I'm a wise man, too. . . .

HENRY: (*hesitantly*)
                        No. Although. . . .
                        If he wants to talk wisely. . . .

DIGNITARY/TRAITOR: (*provokingly*)
                        If he wants to talk wisely. . . .

COURT: (*somnolently*)
                        If
                        if
                        wisely. . . .

HENRY: Very well!

Afternoon tea. LACKEYS *bring in coffee and pastries. The*
DIGNITARIES *break up into groups. The* LADIES *fan themselves
with enormous fans.*

COURT: How pleasant it is at His Majesty's tea
            To carry on a flirt in a form so discreet
            Oh, the toupées and décolletés do the senses arouse
            While His Majesty himself does the honours of the
                        house!

May I offer you some pastries! That's very kind of you. Oh,

what a splendid crowd! I'm terribly sorry. I bow down before you. Oh, what a magnificent gown!

VOICE OF THE FATHER: (*upstage*) All right, give me a little tea too!

A LADY: (*passing by, to a* DIGNITARY) Who is that strange looking character talking with the Crown Prince?

A DIGNITARY: He's a foreign envoy or else an ambassador.

HENRY: All right, give me a little tea too. (*To the* DRUNKARD) May I offer you some pastries?

DRUNKARD: That's very kind of you. I hope nobody is listening.

HENRY: As you can see, they're going out of their way to make this little chat possible . . . in absolute secrecy. . . .

They both walk over to one side of the stage.

DRUNKARD: Well, I'll come straight to the point. . . . I'm not quite as drunk as I appear to be . . . and all these antics of mine are part of a plot to undermine the authority of the King. Many of the dignitaries are conspiring against him, and it was they who dragged me out of prison by the scruff of the neck. But Your Highness spoke just now with such wisdom that. . . .

HENRY: He's trying to flatter me. . . .

DRUNKARD: . . . that all my efforts were for nothing. There was only one thing in all this wisdom which struck me as being not quite so wise. . . . Do you believe in God, Your Highness?

HENRY: (*into space*)
Since he has asked, I have to say no.

DRUNKARD: Well, then how can you let yourself be married by the King? If God does not exist, how can your father be a king? After all, doesn't his power come from God? And this Bishop is not a bishop on his own power either.

HENRY: I already told you. . . . I already answered that. . . . Even if my father were an ordinary madman who only imagined he was King, he is still a defender of virtue and dignity. . . . And

even though I do not believe in God, I do believe in Moral Law
and Human Dignity on earth.

> How solemn I sound!

DRUNKARD: And who established that law if there isn't any
God?

HENRY: Who? People.

DRUNKARD: Then why do you wish to make this such a solemn
occasion if it is merely a product of man's imagination like
everything else?

HENRY: (*flustered*)
> As a matter of fact
> To a certain extent he's right. I don't believe
> In any of this. . . . I behave
> As though I believed in it, and yet I don't believe in it
> I respect it, and yet I don't respect it. . . . I genuflect
> But I don't genuflect. . . . I humble myself
> And yet I don't humble myself
> And I know that all of this is just a farce. And so
> The greater my wisdom, the greater
> My stupidity. . . . Shhh! Shhh! Quiet!
> He mustn't find out about this!

DRUNKARD: Why does Your Highness place him above yourself
if it was you who put him on the throne in the first place?

HENRY: (*to himself*) That's true. And if he is not my King, I am
not his Prince. . . .

DRUNKARD: And the same is true of your fiancée. . . . If it was
you who made him King, and if it was the King who elevated
her to the dignity of a virgin, that would mean it was you, Your
Highness, who made a virgin out of her. . . . And what kind of a
virgin is that, I ask you?

HENRY: It was I who made a virgin out of her. This drunkard has
a pretty clear head on his shoulders. . . . And yet

> If it were really that simple, why
> Do I feel as though I were celebrating

Some sort of elevated mass?

DRUNKARD: A mass?

HENRY: A mass.

DRUNKARD: A mass?

HENRY: A mass.

(*Gravely*) Get away from me: I am a priest. . . .

DRUNKARD: (*slowly*) I am a priest too. . . .

COURT: Oh, the toupées and décolletés do the senses arouse
While His Majesty himself does the honours of the
house!

HENRY: (*sadly*) He's mimicking me, he's mimicking me so as to
make a fool out of me. A moment ago he was talking sense, but
now he's talking nonsense. . . .

DRUNKARD: Nonsense?

HENRY: (*thoughtful*) Nonsense. I thought he was more clever. . . .

DRUNKARD: Clever?

HENRY: Clever.

DRUNKARD: Clever?

HENRY: Clever!

DRUNKARD: (*exploding*)
Now I shall tell you something and cleverly, too
About that religion whose priests we both are.
    Between ourselves
And through ourselves is our God born
And not to heaven, but to earth does our church
    belong
We create God and we alone, whence does arise
That dark and terrestrial, ignorant and bestial
Intimate and inferior, humanly human mass
Whose priest I am!

Both PRIESTS *begin making wild and pathetic gestures.*

HENRY: Whose priest I am?
            But . . . . I don't understand.

DRUNKARD: You don't understand
            And yet somehow you do understand. You
                understand
            Because I understand.

HENRY: You understand
            Because I understand. You? Me? Which of us
            No, no, I don't exactly see. . . .

DRUNKARD: Do you see
            This finger? (*He shows him his finger*)

HENRY: Do you see
            This finger? (*He shows him his finger*)

DRUNKARD: Yes, I see it
            I see that finger!

HENRY: And I see it too!
            Oh, what wisdom, what profundity! It's as though
            I were looking at myself in a thousand mirrors!
            Your finger, my finger!

DRUNKARD: My finger, your finger, your finger, my finger!
                Between ourselves.
            It's between ourselves. Would you like me
            To anoint you priest
            With this finger?

HENRY: Would you like me
            To anoint you priest
            With this finger?

DRUNKARD: Oh, yes, gladly.

HENRY: Oh, yes, gladly.

The DRUNKARD *makes as if to touch him.*

            There's that finger again! You pig!

DRUNKARD: You pig!

HENRY: You pig!

All he ever wants to do is touch me!
(*Checking himself*) May I offer you some pastry?

COURT: How pleasant it is at His Majesty's tea
To carry on a flirt in a form so discreet
Oh, the toupées and décolletés do the senses arouse
While His Majesty himself does the honours of the
house!

HENRY: (*to himself*) Oh, I let myself be taken in by words, and
all this time he just wanted to touch me. I'd touch this moron
who's been trying to make a moron out of me. . . . I'd touch
him and throw him out, but there are too many lights here, too
many women and too many dignitaries. (*He makes for the*
DRUNKARD, *but the* DIGNITARIES *intervene*)

DIGNITARY/TRAITOR: (*to the* DRUNKARD) My dear Ambassador!

A LADY: (*passing by*) Who is that mysterious gentleman who has
been chatting with the Crown Prince for such a long time?

A DIGNITARY: (*emphatically*) He's a foreign envoy or else an
ambassador!

A LADY: An ambassador!

DIGNITARY/TRAITOR: My dear Ambassador!

2nd TRAITOR: Dear Mr Ambassador!

3rd TRAITOR: My dearest Ambassador!

DRUNKARD: (*eloquently*)
Ah, greetings, gentlemen, greetings!

A LADY: My dearest Ambassador Plenipotentiary!

DRUNKARD: I bow down before you, madam.

Ceremonious bows.

HENRY: Hmmm. . . . A few minutes ago he was just a drunkard,
and now he's an ambassador. I'd touch him, but I have no
desire to make a fool of myself. One has to keep up appearances.

DRUNKARD: Forgive me, ladies and gentlemen, but I would like to have just a few more words with the Crown Prince. Then I shall be completely at your service.

TRAITORS: We shall not disturb you, Your Excellency. (*Deep bows; they withdraw*)

DRUNKARD: (*to* HENRY) This is indeed a magnificent reception!

HENRY: Indeed it is.

COURT: Oh, the toupées and décolletés do the senses arouse
While His Majesty himself does the honours of the house!

The AMBASSADOR *and the* PRINCE *stroll back and forth with this elegant reception in the background.*

DRUNKARD: (*in the style of a diplomat*) In regard to what we were just saying, His Highness will be pleased to observe. . . . Please believe me when I say that albeit I am a foreign ambassador, still do I harbour the most fervent feelings of devotion and respect for the person of His Royal Majesty. On the other hand, I should say it is precisely on account of this feeling of love and respect that I fear . . . or rather, I suspect . . . and to a certain extent even know . . . that many of your eminent dignitaries have of late estranged themselves, so to speak, from the throne. . . .

HENRY: (*diplomatically*) Is that so?

DRUNKARD: As a sincere friend and devoted servant of the royal family I consider it well-nigh my duty to apprise Your Highness of this state of affairs in a confidential manner.

HENRY: I am extremely indebted to you, Mr Ambassador.

DRUNKARD: There is no question, Your Highness, but that your father is a great monarch, or so it would seem to me at least . . . but it is not at all inconceivable, I am afraid, that his concept of power is not altogether consistent with the spirit of modern times.

DIGNITARY/TRAITOR: You could not have couched it any better, Mr Ambassador.

DRUNKARD: That he is a grand and imposing figure cannot be disputed, but the anachronism of his concepts is all too evident — an anachronism, I might add, which is peculiar to persons more advanced in years. (*In a confidential manner*) But really, Your Highness — to believe in some code of morality and decency that has been laid down once and for all? Between you and me, modern man must be exceedingly more flexible; modern man knows that there is nothing permanent or absolute, but that everything is forever creating itself anew . . . creating itself between individuals . . . creating itself. . . .

HENRY: One cannot deny that you are a flexible person and that you are constantly creating yourself anew. . . .

DRUNKARD: Looking at it objectively. . . . But let's have something to drink, eh? To His Majesty's health!

DIGNITARY/TRAITOR: To His Majesty's health!

HENRY: To His Majesty's health!

DRUNKARD: Let's see, what were we talking about?. . . Ah, yes. . . . It is for that very reason that not a few of the dignitaries have, so to say, estranged themselves . . . ha, ha, ha, but His Majesty's greatest enemy is yourself, Your Highness. . . .

HENRY: Me?

DRUNKARD: Ha, ha, ha! Because the admiration which your noble qualities arouse. . . .

HENRY: He's trying to flatter me. . . .

DRUNKARD: (*in a confidential manner*) Many people here believe you are the one who ought to be in power. . . . But let's have something to drink, eh Prince? To His Majesty's health!

DIGNITYAR/TRAITOR: To His Majesty's health! Many people here have no other desire — after a very long life for His Majesty — save that of seeing you in power. . . .

DRUNKARD: And then His Highness could grant himself a marriage . . . or even do without a marriage altogether, ha, ha, ha — instead of submitting to these old-fashioned ceremonies!

DIGNITARY/TRAITOR: Let's have another glass! Goodness but that wine is strong . . . it makes one teeter . . . like a king on his throne. . . .

DRUNKARD: Ha, ha, ha! As a matter of fact, it seems it would suffice to touch glasses!

DIGNITARY/TRAITOR: To touch glasses in the presence of the entire Court!

DRUNKARD: Then, if someone touched the King. . . .

DIGNITARY/TRAITOR: Quite unexpectedly!

DRUNKARD: Touched. . . .

DIGNITARY/TRAITOR: Just like that, in front of everybody! For all to see!

DRUNKARD: Ha, ha, ha! But nobody's going to touch the King because everyone is afraid of the Prince's anger and wisdom. It's only natural for a son to defend his father. . . .

DIGNITARY/TRAITOR: Another glass! But what if the Prince himself . . . if the Prince himself went up to him and . . . . I didn't really mean that, though you must admit it's a tempting idea. . . . I confess that whenever I see such an untouchable person . . . damn it, I don't know why, I always get the urge . . . to go up and . . . er . . . well . . . touch him, see? With my finger. Hm, hm. . . .

DRUNKARD: Ha, ha, ha, ha, ha! And there's his fiancée standing behind him and, damn it, she's untouchable too. . . . Untouchable! Oh, if I could just touch him with one finger at least, with just one little finger, oh, oh, oh, and ha, ha, ha!

HENRY: Finger!
           (*calmly*) There's that idiotic finger again!
           You pig!

DRUNKARD: (*gloomily*)
           You pig!

HENRY: You pig!
           May I offer you some pastry?

COURT: How pleasant it is at His Majesty's tea
To carry on a flirt in a form so discreet. . . .

HENRY: And you would like me
To touch the King . . . with my finger. . . . Because
    if I touch the King
Then you'll touch him too, right?. . . You'd have me
Commit treason . . . is that it?

BOTH: Oh, oh!
That was just the wine in us speaking. . . . A drop of
    that stuff
And a man's liable to say anything!

HENRY: You bloody drunken swine, you're trying to get me
drunk. . . . Well, in a second I'll prove to you and to myself
how sober I am . . . that's right, sober. This intrigue is absurd.
But this absurdity is likewise deceiving. Because this intrigue
is so irrational, so obviously contrived that even if I rejected
your rather naive propositions, in the end I would come out
looking just as ridiculous as if I'd agreed to them. That's what
you had in mind all along, isn't it? And so I hereby declare
both to you and to myself that I regard none of this seriously —
neither you, nor this conversation, nor the title of this man who
only a short while ago was nothing but an ordinary drunkard. I
don't give a damn about the lot of you! And if I stand here
talking to you instead of pouncing on you and touching you —
it's only because I wish to keep up appearances and, if possible, avoid a scandal. . . So there! Am I sober or not?

DRUNKARD: A glass of Burgundy or a glass of Tokay!

DIGNITARY/TRAITOR:
    A glass of Tokay or a glass of port!

HENRY: Of course I'm sober! I could wake up at any moment
and annihilate you all — but I don't wish to spoil this magnificent and intoxicating reception . . . and besides, then my
fiancée would disappear too, evaporate. . . Understand?

DRUNKARD: Burgundy, Burgundy!

DIGNITARY/TRAITOR:
    Tokay, Tokay!

HENRY: I am the most sober person in the world! I am behaving
in the same manner as you are, but with full awareness, so-
berly, ha, ha, ha . . . . I am behaving in the same manner as you
are, because to tell the truth, all of this gives me pleasure. . . .

> Words tickle me, thoughts caress me, the passions
>   get stronger
> Everything is spinning . . . singing . . . ringing
> Oh, this sea of lights, this ocean of words
> And I'm drowning in it, drowning, drowning . . .
>   like a drunkard
> (See how sober I am!?)
> I'm unsteady on my feet and I'm seeing three of
>   everything
> I'm hearing things and my vision's getting blurry
> It's almost as though I understood, but I don't
>   understand. . . .
> Noise. Noise. And in this noise
> One thought alone persists: keep up appearances

Don't let anyone catch on you're drunk, ha, ha. (See how lucid
I am!?) And don't let anyone know you're a drunkard.
And so, if anyone addresses me in a polite tone, I'll answer him
with extreme politeness, ah, ah, yes, yes!
And if anyone begins speaking to me in a serious tone, ho, ho,
yes indeed, yes indeed!
And if anyone starts behaving toward me like a drunkard, I'll
behave toward him like a drunkard too, hee, hee, hic, hic! (You
can see for yourselves how lucid I am. . . .)

DRUNKARD: (*drunk*)
> Son-of-a . . . oh, f-f-f-fiddlesticks!
> Shit!

HENRY: Wait a minute, wait a minute
> I'll show you even more clearly how sober I am.
>   Let's assume
> You are soused too — and that everyone here
> Is a little . . . hmm. . . . One person gets drunk by
>   means of another
> While each would pretend he's as sober as I. Ha, ha, ha!

> But if that were the case, then this is all a farce!

One drunkard, in order to pretend he's sober, adapts himself to
the drunkenness of another who, in order to pretend he's sober,
adapts himself to the drunkenness of still another drunkard who. . . .

> And consequently all of this is just a lie! Nobody says
> What he wants to say, only what's considered proper.
>   Words
> Join together behind our backs like traitors
> And it is not we who say words, but words which
>   say us
> And betray our thoughts, which in turn betray
> Our treasonous feelings. . . . Oh, treason!
> (*Drunk*) Incessant treason!

DRUNKARD: (*picking up the thread*) That's right, treason!

DIGNITARY/TRAITOR:
> Treason! Down with the King!
> Down with the King!

TRAITORS: (*gathering around them, in an undertone*)
> Down with the King!

HENRY: Traitors! That's not what I wanted to say!

DIGNITARY/TRAITOR: (*in the voice of a conspirator*)
> Gentlemen, the Prince is with us! Down with the
>   King!
> Long live the new King!

DRUNKARD: Down with the King!

HENRY *and the* CONSPIRATORS *advance toward the* KING. *The*
GUESTS *make way, revealing the* KING, *who is taking his tea in
the company of the* QUEEN *and* MOLLY. JOHNNY *is standing
nearby.*

HENRY: That's not what I wanted to say!

COURT: How pleasant it is at His Majesty's tea
>   To carry on a flirt in a form so discreet
>   Oh, the toupées and décolletés do the senses arouse

> While His Majesty himself does the honours of the house!

FATHER: (*uneasy, seeing the* DRUNKARD *approach*) Now what does he want?

HENRY: This gentleman is a foreign envoy or else an ambassador!

FATHER: An ambassador, eh? Whatever you do, don't make a fool of yourself. . . . (*Aloud*) It is indeed a pleasure, Your Excellency, to welcome you under our roof.

DRUNKARD: I am both honoured and flattered, Your Majesty. (*He bows down before* MOLLY) Permit me, O loveliest of maidens, to adorn the bosom of your best man with the flower of my chivalrous homage.

MOLLY: Thank you.

FATHER: It is my sincerest wish, Mr Ambassador, that relations between our two powerful governments in accord with international harmony and co-operation and with a view to consolidating and safeguarding, as well as everlasting peace which for centuries has constituted the guiding principle, and in the interest of mankind. If you touch me, you pig, I'll clobber you in the kisser and slap you in irons.

DRUNKARD: The consolidation and safeguarding as well as mankind in the spirit of co-operation and in the interest of everlasting peace constitutes the guiding and inviolable principle of our peaceful aspirations that are enlivened by the spirit of mutual understanding. I'm going to touch you, see. . . . I'm going to blow myself up, you pig, and lay you out flat. . . .

FATHER: May I offer you some pastry?

DRUNKARD: That's terribly kind of you. (*To* HENRY, *aside*) Quick! Now's the time! Stick your finger in his belly!

HENRY: My father?

DRUNKARD: Then afterwards *you* will be King!

HENRY: (*musingly*) Me?

The stage becomes motionless.

I'm only joking, of course. . . . But what if. . . . To overthrow
this father and seize power! To be in control of the situation! To
be in control!
Everything keeps slipping away from me! It's terrible! I am no
longer master of the situation! I'm like a puppet in a puppet
show. To control! Oh, if only I had control!
To govern!
No, no, I was only joking, of course. . . . But what if I were to
overthrow this King! What do I need him for anyway? I made
him King so he could grant me a marriage. But why should I let
myself be married by someone else? If I were to become master, I
could grant myself a marriage — and a decent and respectable
one too. Then I would be the one who makes laws. I would be the
one who decides what is holy, what is virtuous, what is a sacrament — I would be the one who decides everything!
Oh, God! If only I could be in control!
Oh, God! What God? Oh, Father! What father? It was I who
made them what they are. By virtue of my bounty! By virtue of
my will! Why should I kneel down before them? Why not
kneel down before myself, myself, myself, the sole source of
my law? Shhh!. . . Don't say that. Why do you say that? You're
only repeating what he (*points to the* DRUNKARD) said.

> Well so what if he said it? I'll destroy him too!
> It is I who create kings!
> It is I who should be King!
> I am supreme! There is nothing higher than me!
> I am God!

And it is my finger, my finger, which. . . . (*Frightened*) No, it
isn't true! I didn't mean it! It isn't true! I wouldn't betray my
father for anything in the world! My King!

(*To the* DRUNKARD) I shall not betray him!

DRUNKARD: You won't betray him, you pig?

FATHER: (*who has been listening*) What, what, what?. . . Treason?. . .

HENRY: That's not what I wanted to say!

FATHER: Don't you come near me!

HENRY: I'm not coming near you.

FATHER: Don't move! Don't anybody move!

HENRY: I'm not moving. (*Despairingly*) Why are you afraid of me?

FATHER: Me? Henry, my son, my child, how could I be afraid of you, my friend, my defender, my support? No, no, Henry, I'm not afraid. . . .

HENRY: Calm yourself. . . .

FATHER: Adjust my sash, oh, oh,
Adjust my sash. . .

HENRY: (*adjusting the sash*)
He's trembling, his heart is pounding and his cheeks
Are bathed with sweat. . . .

FATHER: (*quietly*) Tssst . . . . Henry. . . .

HENRY: What is it?

FATHER: You'd better go away. . . . Go away.

HENRY: Why?

FATHER: Henry, why should I be afraid of you?. . . Oh, perhaps just a little bit, just a tiny bit, maybe just a teeny-weeny bit — you know, just in case. . . . But I am the King, Henry, so I think you'd better leave me now, because even though it's small, being royal it might grow . . . it might become gigantic . . . and then one day it might explode! And the King and me might get carried away!

HENRY: Calm down. . . . Control yourself. . . .

FATHER: How can I control myself if I am . . . greater than myself?

HENRY: Shhh!. . . Don't shout!

FATHER: I'm not shouting

It's my voice which is shouting! Tssst. . . . (*In a loud voice*)

Thank you, my son, for your loyalty! I know in your filial heart
there isn't any treason. No, there isn't any! I haven't the slightest bit of doubt. Not the slightest . . . and if I say I haven't any
doubts, it's not because

> I have any; and I emphasize
> That I say it not because of that, it's just
> So nobody will think I'm coming back to it

For some other reason. But what I just got through explaining
should likewise not be interpreted as a sign of

> My distrust. (*To the* DIGNITARIES) Stop
> Listening to me! Why
> Do you listen to me all the time? Why

Don't you stop gawping at me? Do you think it's very pleasant
to be listened to and gawped at all the time? Get out of here,
out, out!

> No, no, stay here! I
> Have nothing to hide. If I tell you
> To get out, it does not mean at all

that I have something to hide. No, no, I don't have any doubts as
far as my son is concerned; I am positive he is not a traitor, I have
no doubts whatsoever, none whatsoever. . . . For if I had even the
slightest bit of doubt in this respect, even so much as the slightest
then this tiny grain of doubt would in the presence of so many,
many people and the expectation of so many, many people . . .
this doubt, I say, this tiny, insignificant doubt . . . would become
larger . . . just a tiny bit larger . . . and that larger doubt would
provoke a light trembling which, being a royal trembling, would
provoke a great panic . . . and then an even greater one . . . greater
than me even . . . and that panic would carry me away, because
the King is carrying me away! And if the King trembles, I cannot
stop him from trembling! And if the King shouts, I cannot make
him lower his voice! And the King, the King, the King is shouting: treason! Treason! Treason!

COURT: Treason!

HENRY: Treason!

FATHER: Help! Guards! Guards!

The GUARDS *rush in.*

> He has a finger!
> Oh, treason, treason, treason!

HENRY: (*touching the* FATHER *with his finger*)
> Arrest
> Arrest this father of mine! And cast him
> Into some dark and dreary,
> Foul and oppressive
> Godforsaken dungeon!
> (*Despairingly*) That's not what I wanted to say!

DRUNKARD: (*with delight*) He toushhed him! He toushhed him in the belly! (*He makes as though he is going to attack the* FATHER)

HENRY: (*To* JOHNNY, *indicating the* DRUNKARD)
> Arrest
> This pig! And into the dungeon with him!
> (*To everyone*) I don't know how it happened
> But it happened! I betrayed
> My father!
> (*To the* DRUNKARD) What time is it?

DRUNKARD: Seven.

FATHER: (*groaning*)
> Henreee. . . .

COURT: (*thunderously*)
> Oh, Henry!

HENRY: (*thunderously*)
> Oh, Henry!
> Now *I* am King!
> Bind him, break his bones and trample him under
>   foot!

The GUARDS *arrest the* FATHER.

MOTHER: (*in a shrill voice*) Henry, dear, what are you doing?

HENRY: Now I shall rule! I alone!

I shall get married on my own! And nobody is going to stand in
my way! I've just had the old man placed under arrest. That
drunkard has likewise been taken into custody. Now I am King,
now I am the one who is in control, now I shall get married on
my own. . . .

> Enough of this idle chatter! Do you think
> That I am blind? That I don't see

How you're trying to make a chump out of me? But that's all
over now. I'm not going to dance to your tune any more. I'm
not going to be your puppet on a string. I'll force you to obey
and respect my will. If the old man's afraid to rule, if he's
unable to marry me, I'll get married by myself. Where is my
fiancée? (*Seeing* MOLLY *approach*)

> Ah, here she comes. She has ceased to be pure
> But don't worry, I shall purify her! I shall lead her
>   out of here!
> I shall grant myself a marriage! I alone!
> Let nobody try to interfere! I shall do it myself!
> Because I am alone here, I am alone here
> And none of you are here!

Procession. HENRY *and* MOLLY *lead. Wedding march.*

> I am marching at the head. . . . What do I care
> If the others are trailing behind me like a tail
> I cannot see them. I am passing
> Through pure space, an empty void. . . .

Noticing the DRUNKARD *who is being guarded by* JOHNNY.

And get that imbecile out of here, eliminate him. . . . Do away
with him . . . you won't get off very easily with me. . . . Sen-
tence him to death!

DRUNKARD: (*in the voice of a beggar*) Master. . . . Master. . . .

HENRY: That sounded pretty silly, didn't it?. . . Well, you won't
be doing me any more harm where you're going!

DRUNKARD: Your Majesty! Ah, what's the use! So much the
worse for me! Very well. So be it then! (*To everyone*) They're

going to hang me, they're going to hang me! That's all they've
been doing around here for the last few years — hanging
people! (*To* HENRY) Sire, I have but one request to make before
I die. That I might be permitted to have one last look at her.

HENRY: Who?

DRUNKARD: My Queen.

HENRY: I bet he's up to another one of his tricks. But I am not
afraid any more — everything is dependent on my will now.

> All right, go ahead.
> You're looking at her.

DRUNKARD: (*to himself*) Oh, Molly, Molly — would I like to
have a slug of you!

HENRY: (*to himself*) Ha, ha, ha!

DRUNKARD: I didn't marry you, and now it's someone else's
turn.

HENRY: Let him say whatever he pleases. (*To* JOHNNY) Keep a
close watch on him.

DRUNKARD: If I didn't have this joker on my back, if I hadn't
been arrested — I'd've known how to . . . with you, me, me and
you. . . .

HENRY: He's talking gibberish.

DRUNKARD: I shall carry the image of your angelic face with me
always unto the four walls of my coffin, and there with your
image before me I shall turn up my toes . . . hic. . . . (*To*
HENRY) Sire, I beseech you to grant me this one last favour —
ask this young fellow here (*points to* JOHNNY) to take a flower
out of that vase and hold it a little bit above Her Majesty's
precious little head while I stand over here and watch.

HENRY: This is another of his idiotic pranks, but if I refuse
everyone will get the idea I'm afraid . . . so I'd better not
refuse. (*To* JOHNNY) Do as he says. (*To* MOLLY) My dearest
Mary, I trust you will see it in your heart to grant this pathetic
maniac his last dying wish.

DRUNKARD: Oh, my Queen! My only wish is to die with your image before my eyes. . . . I humbly entreat you to hold the flower jus' a little bit lower . . . so it barely comes down over her eyes. . . . (*While lowering the flower,* JOHNNY *embraces* MARY) Now just a little bit lower . . . that's it, that's it. . . . Oh, my Queen!

HENRY: What's he trying to prove? It doesn't mean a thing.

DIGNITARIES: (*waking up, theatrically*)
               It doesn't mean a thing
               It's quite harmless!
               Poor soul!
               It's rather amusing.

DRUNKARD: Excuse me, jus' a little bit lower . . . so the flower barely touches her neck. . . . Oh, that's it, that's it, perfect. . . . Oh, how ravishing. . . .

DIGNITARIES: One must admire the patience of His Majesty.
               Not only is he just but he's generous too.
               One must admire the patience of Her Majesty
               Her Majesty is exceedingly generous!

DRUNKARD: (*unexpectedly, gravely*) And now don't either of you move, 'cos I'm going to take away the flower. (*He pulls the flower out of* JOHNNY*'s hand*) Don't move. . . .

MOLLY: This is just like posing for a photograph.

HENRY: (*to* JOHNNY *and* MOLLY) Wait a second. (*To himself*) Well, so what? (*To* JOHNNY) Don't move. (*To himself*) I wonder what he's up to?

        This is absurd. I thought he was more clever. . . .

DRUNKARD: Clever.

HENRY: Clever?

DRUNKARD: Clever. . . .

HENRY: What do you mean, clever? What's so clever about that? The flower's already been discarded and they're still standing in the same artificial position. . . . Clever?

DRUNKARD: Clever. . . .

HENRY: Clever?

                What of it? They're standing there together. . . . So?
                    They're standing together. . . .
                Ah, the two of them together. . . . He with her, and
                    she
                With him. . . . Well, so what if they are? Together
                But it doesn't make any sense. . . . They're standing
                    there in an artificial manner. Wait a minute. . . .
                Well, what of it?. . . They're standing there, and the
                    rest of us
                Are looking on. . . . While they go on standing
                    there. . . .
                You pig!
                You've bound them together
                By a dreadful
                And inferior bond. You've married them
                You pig priest!

DRUNKARD: You pig!

HENRY: You pig!

Laughter of the DIGNITARIES.

ACT THREE

A hall in the castle; HENRY *and the* CHANCELLOR.

CHANCELLOR: There is peace. All the rebellious elements are under arrest. Assembly has also been taken into custody along with military and civilian circles, vast segments of the population, the High Court, the Joint Chiefs of Staff, Boards and Departments, all public and private authorities, the press, hospitals and orphanages. All the Ministries have been placed under arrest, and everything else besides; in short, Your Majesty — everything. The police have likewise been imprisoned. There is peace. Quiet. It's humid.

HENRY: Indeed. There is peace. How calm it is.

CHANCELLOR: Well, what did you expect? It's autumn.

HENRY: Where is the Chief of Police?

CHANCELLOR: He's waiting.

HENRY: Well, as long as he's waiting, let him wait. And what about my father, the ex-King?

CHANCELLOR: Under arrest.

HENRY: And that . . . drunkard?

CHANCELLOR: Under arrest.

HENRY: (*gloomily, bitterly*) Today's the wedding. . . . What a miserable day!

CHANCELLOR: A day like any other.

HENRY: You're getting old.

CHANCELLOR: I'm afraid so.

HENRY: I am in power.
           Never mind how I came by it. I took control
           Of the situation . . . and so everything will be
           As I command. . . . Therefore I command
           Everyone to assemble here, in this hall, because
              the King has decided
           To bestow a marriage on himself.
           Now take those louts by the snouts and drag them
              in here!

CHANCELLOR: Yes, Your Majesty.

HENRY: Have my father brought in under heavy guard. By the
         snout. I wish to get married in his presence.

CHANCELLOR: Yes, Your Majesty.

HENRY: And have my mother brought in, too. By the snout.

CHANCELLOR: Yes, Your Majesty.

HENRY: And that drunkard too . . but securely bound, mind you. I
         want everyone to be present when I administer the sacrament to
         myself. I'm not afraid of anybody. Nobody can do me any
         harm. I alone know what I must do, and that's that. I am in
         command now and so everything will be done according to my
         will. I am in control; I am in control of the situation. If any-
         body conspires against me or tries to commit acts of sabotage,
         take the lout by the snout and. . . . Has the Chief of Police
         arrived with his henchmen? Show them in.

Enter the CHIEF OF POLICE *and three of his* HENCHMEN.

HENRY: Just what I needed! Look at these snouts! Ho, ho, these
         snouts will take them by the snouts! Yes Sir! If anybody gets
         out of line or in any way tries to interfere or cause trouble, take
         the lout by the snout and slap him silly in front of everybody
         . . . for all to see. . . .

CHANCELLOR: I'm afraid, Sire, that. . . . Let's see, what was it I
         wanted to say?

HENRY: My head is clear. Listen to my way of reasoning. Please,
         listen to my way of reasoning. I have already lost my inno-

cence. They robbed me of my virginity. Lately, though, I've been doing a lot of thinking on my own. I didn't sleep a wink last night!

Holiness, majesty, power, law, morality, love, ridiculousness, stupidity, wisdom — all these come from people in the same way that wine comes from grapes. Like wine, understand? I have the situation well in hand and I shall force these apes to produce everything my heart desires. And if that is ridiculous, I'll take that ridiculousness by the snout too! And if that is foolish, I'll take that foolishness by the snout too! And if God, old antediluvian God, has anything against it, I'll take him by the snout too!...

CHANCELLOR & CHIEF: Yes, Your Majesty!

HENCHMEN: Yes, Your Majesty!

HENRY: Yes, Your Majesty!

ALL: Yes, Your Majesty!

Enter PANDULF.

PANDULF: No!

HENRY: No?

PANDULF: No!

HENRY: Well, I'll be d. . . . If it isn't the Bishop!

PANDULF: I am Pandulf.
          A cardinal of the Roman Catholic Church, and I
              declare this
          To your face, you infamous usurper: God exists
          And a marriage not consecrated by the Church
          Is not a marriage, but a sacrilege!

HENRY: Ha, ha, ha, Pandulf, Pandulf!

PANDULF: Yes, I am Pandulf.

HENRY: Ah . . . and you're
         A cardinal too, if I'm not mistaken?. . .

PANDULF: I am a servant of God
           A servant of God, I, Pandulf. . . .

HENRY: My dear Pandulf, you aren't by any chance . . . a
                little tipsy
                Tipsy
                Tipsy
                With this Pandulf of yours? Well? My dear Pandulf,
                you aren't a little bit tight
                Tight
                Tight
                With the cardinal of yours? The cardinal has gone
                to your head. Booze
                Booze
                Booze

But my dear Pandulf, you are absolutely blind drunk with your
Lord God and the Holy Catholic Church. You're nothing but an
ordinary drunkard, Pandulf. Shame on you! Oh, I know all
about it. First one glass, then another, pretty soon — away you
go! No Pandulf, you're no ordinary fellow. You're a drunkard!

PANDULF: I curse
                You!

HENRY: What? Are you taking nips again? Are you getting
    pickled on your own curse in my presence? Well, this has gone
    far enough. I'm going to touch you. (*He touches him*)

PANDULF: Oh, God. . . .

HENRY: Arrest this boozy priest!
                Arrest him. Come on, henchmen,
                Take him by the snout!

    PANDULF *is whisked offstage by the* HENCHMEN.

                What a miserable day!

CHANCELLOR: Yes, it's a miserable day. . . .

HENRY: I am ruling. . . .

CHANCELLOR: Yes, Your Majesty.

HENRY: I shall rule. . . .

CHANCELLOR: Yes, Your Majesty.

HENRY: I'm going to touch everybody.

CHANCELLOR: Yes, Your Majesty.

HENRY: No one will dare to touch me. . . . By the way,
                My dear Chancellor,
                Tell me, people aren't by any chance making fun of
                    me a little
                Are they?. . .

CHANCELLOR: Oh, oh, oh!

CHIEF: Oh, oh, oh!

HENRY: They aren't saying
                Behind my back somewhere, and
                Behind their own backs too, that . . . that . . . that. . . .
                That I'm jealous, for example, ha, ha! Well, are
                    they? That would be
                A laugh, wouldn't it?

CHANCELLOR: Oh, oh, oh!

CHIEF: Oh, oh, oh!

HENRY: I only ask
                On account of that silly little episode
                With the flower, ha, ha, ha! The insinuation
                Made by that contemptible drunkard left little room
                    for doubt
                And may have given more fodder
                To these foul and slippery tongues, ha, ha, ha!

CHANCELLOR: I know nothing about it!

CHIEF: We know nothing about it!

HENRY: Because
                If he connected them in such a singular position
                Then they are connected . . . and perhaps others
                Are likewise connecting them . . . her with him, and
                    him
                With her. . . Well? Speak up! Perhaps
                No one will have the nerve to say it openly

> But that won't stop them from smirking, insinuat
>   ing, or winking with one eye,
> Exchanging meaningful glances or signalling on the
>   sly, ha, ha, ha. . . .

My throat is dry. My throat has gone dry. Hey, servant, bring me an apple! I'm going to have an apple! (*To the* CHANCEL-LOR) Well? Well?

CHANCELLOR: Properly speaking, Your Majesty, everyone is acting properly, but then again, properly speaking, perhaps improperly too, who knows; perhaps people are insinuating things, and then again, maybe they aren't, how should I know, I'm nearsighted, my vision isn't what it used to be. . . .

HENRY: You blind old nag! You blind old mole!

CHIEF: I'm nearsighted too.

HENRY: I'll let the air out of both of you. . . . (*To the* SERVANT *who has brought the apple*) Wait a moment. Stand still, let me get a good look at you. Who knows what this man might be

> Thinking

In private, up there. . . . Look at him! He's a numskull, one of those shady types. But who knows? Perhaps

> He's imagining something. Perhaps in his mind
> He's connecting. . . .
> He's connecting the two of them there. . . .
> Perhaps he's making fun of me in private
> And betraying me . . . with him . . . and with her. . . .
> Oh, the traitors!

They're betraying me! They're nothing but a bunch of traitors! And this immobile face. How do I know but at this very moment he isn't laughing at me or insinuating something awful, whether inwardly he isn't howling with laughter. . . . This apple is lying *between* my knife and fork. Knife and fork. What's it doing *between* my knife and fork? Oh, yes, of course, that's how they always serve apples, peaches, pears. . . . No, besides it's absurd. There was never anything between Johnny and her. . . . No, it just my imagination. . . . I know it's idiotic and yet

I have to say it . . . and saying it
I declare it. . . .

CHANCELLOR: (*to the* CHIEF)
His Majesty
Is curiously absorbed with his thoughts. . . .

CHIEF: He's probably
Troubled by unwholesome dreams.

HENRY: (*to himself*)
I don't want to drink any more
I'm not going to drink any more. . . .

CHANCELLOR: (*aside*)
Tch, tch, tch, vodka, vodka!

HENRY: (*to himself*)

Until now perhaps
There has never been anything between them, but
      now
That everybody connects them, maybe he connects
      himself
With her too. . . . And connecting himself with her
Touches her. . . .

CHANCELLOR:
Oh, oh, oh, vodka, vodka. . . .

HENRY: (*to himself*)
I hear what I'm saying
And I hear what he's saying. And I know perfectly
      well
That what we're both saying is pure comedy
All the same, I must speak. . . .

CHANCELLOR: (*delightedly, aloud*)
The king is sozzled!

HENRY: (*to the* CHANCELLOR) Shut your trap! (*He slaps the*
   CHIEF OF POLICE *in the face*)

CHIEF: Why me?

HENRY: Just to keep you guessing! At the moment
           I am in need of a little brutality — and I'm
                searching for it

In your face! If I'd struck the Chancellor, I would have been
acting only justly. But I want to be brutal! I'm going to establish order here! (*Cries are heard*) Now what's the matter?

MOTHER: (*offstage*)
                Let go of me, let go!

                (*She bursts in*)

                Oh, Henry, my little Henry, your father, your
                     father, your father!

HENRY: Has she gone mad?

MOTHER: Oh, Henry, your father's yelling, your father's
                screaming
                Ranting and raving like an animal, jumping up
                And down!

HENRY: He must have gone crazy!

MOTHER: (*dramatically, lyrically*)
                He tried to break loose, he tried to escape
                Far, far away, into the hills
                But they caught 'im
                And now they're whippin' his ass
                Oh, Henry, he's a pain in your ass!

HENRY: So? What's that got to do with me?

MOTHER: Oh, a knife, a knife, a knife!

HENRY: I hold my knife this way.

MOTHER: (*terrified*)
                For God's sake, Henry!
                I'm your mother!

HENRY: That's right — you are my mother. What a happy coinci-
        dence. . . . (*He walks up to her*) I'd like to hug you and kiss
        you, mamma. . . . (*He puts his arms around her*)

MOTHER: Henry, what are you doing?

HENRY: I'm hugging you.

MOTHER: You'd better leave me alone
There's something odd about the way you hug me
No, no, leave me in peace!

CHANCELLOR: That's odd, that's odd. . . .

CHIEF: Odd, positively distasteful. . . .

FATHER *bursts in, followed by the* HENCHMEN.

FATHER: Help! They're beating me!

MOTHER: Murderers!

FATHER: (*quietly*)
They beat me
(*Louder*) They beat me
(*Shouting*) They beat me! Me! Me!

MOTHER: Come here, he beat me too.

FATHER: (*shouting*) What? What? Has he been beating you?

MOTHER: Quiet, quiet, shh. . . .

FATHER: (*in a lower voice*) Just for that I'll curse the son-of-a. . . .

MOTHER: Shh! Shh!

FATHER: What? What was that you said? He hit you?

HENRY: Lucky thing I have this knife. . . .

ALL: Oh!

HENRY: No, what an idea! I'm not going to kill anyone,
even though this knife
Is sharpening me!
I'm not going to kill anyone — I'm merely going
To touch them. . . .
(*He touches his* MOTHER *and* FATHER)
O cruel and abominable couple
Who would their own son curse! Father and mother!

Holy of holies! But
I am touching them
Look how I'm touching them, look how I'm moving
    them, look how I'm digging into their gut!

CHANCELLOR:
Never before
Have my poor old eyes
Seen such a sight. . . .

CHIEF: Never in a million years
Would I have imagined anything like this!

A HENCHMAN: What a disgrace!

FATHER: May you perish!

MOTHER: Would that your mother had suffered a miscarriage!

FATHER: May your father strangle you to death!

MOTHER: May you never have any children!

FATHER: May your children turn you out in your old age!

MOTHER: May they strangle you to death!

FATHER: May they pluck out your eyes!

HENRY: Take them away!
They're drunk, drunk on motherhood and
    fatherhood!
But I am sober!

The HENCHMEN *converge upon the* MOTHER *and* FATHER.

FATHER: Henreee. . . .

HENRY: What is it?

FATHER: Henre-e-e

Henr-r-r, Henr-e-e-e, I realize you've taken the King away
from me . . . but I'm still your father after all. . . . For God's
sake, Henry, don't deprive me of the father, because if you do,
the universe will burst into smithereens with such an
earsplitting, god-awful racket. . . .

HENRY: Father is a title the same as King is. Can't you speak like an ordinary man? Must you always get dressed up in some title or other?

              I feel sleepy. Take them away!

FATHER: With these words
              You open the gates to a terrible misfortune
              Oh, Lord

MOTHER: Have mercy. . . .

CHANCELLOR: On us sinners. . . . (*He pulls a newspaper out of his pocket*) War has been declared!

HENRY: What? What war?

CHANCELLOR:
              I received this newspaper
              Only a moment ago.

Silence. In the distance, sounds of a cannon exploding.

HENRY: It's true — they're shooting.

FATHER: It sounds like it's coming from the forest. . . .

General anxiety.

MOTHER: We'd better start packing.

CHANCELLOR: If necessary we can go down into the basement.

FATHER: Artillery is nothing. The worst is poison gas. We'd better stock up on supplies. . . . (*To* MOTHER) Go out and buy whatever you can — the stores will be closed soon.

MOTHER: I've got some gas masks around here somewhere . . . but where? I've got them somewhere, but I can't remember . . . which drawer it was. . . . (*With growing uneasiness*) Where have I been keeping them?

An explosion.

CHIEF: It's getting closer.

CHANCELLOR: Sire, will you give
              The orders?

HENRY: I'm not giving any orders, because none of this is real!

> It isn't real! But it *is* real!
> (*Straining his ear*)
> Oh, listen to them fight!

FATHER: What'll become of us? What'll become of us now? Oh, misfortune, conflagration, rape, torture, infamy, dishonour. . . .

HENRY: That's a lot of rubbish! Just some sort
> Of drunken ravings! They're both reeking
> With liquor! Throw them out!

FATHER: (*drunk*)

> Hic! . . . I'm drunk. . . . Hic!. . . So be it then
> My son has said so. . . . Well, such is life. . . .
> But seeing as I'm already a little tight, then before
>   you stick me in the
> Dungeon, what do you say me and you have a little
> Snort, eh? I'm going to let you in on a little secret!
>   I'm going to whishper something in your ear
> That'll go straight to your head. . . .

MOTHER: (*drunk*) Tra-la-la. . . .

FATHER: Don't marry that girl!

> That old drunk was telling you the truth. She
> Used to whore around with your friend Johnny.

HENRY: That's a lie!

FATHER: I'm telling you the truth!

I didn't want to tell you before because I was too ashamed, but seeing as everything has gone to hell anyway. . . .

> On the very same day
> You and she got engaged, I
> Caught 'em in the bushes, stumbled across 'em
>   in the bushes,
> And stepped on 'em with my foot!

HENRY: It isn't true!

> And yet it *is* true!

MOTHER: I caught 'em too once
                Snuggled up together by the well
                They were playin' footsie with each other
                Right there in broad daylight! Don't marry that
                    girl, Henry!

Sound of an explosion.

HENRY: They've started up again!

FATHER: (*looking out the window*) Soldiers.

CHANCELLOR: Soldiers.

MOTHER: They're just kids. Wet behind the ears.

FATHER: Maybe so, but they're already bleeding.

MOTHER: Henry, don't you marry that girl!
                She used to smile at the younger ones too
                She used to fool around with the younger ones too!

FATHER: She bled a lot
                With men younger than she!

MOTHER: In the bushes
                Under some tree, or in the hay. . . .

FATHER: In the cellar!

MOTHER: Or in the attic!

FATHER: In the barn!

MOTHER: Or in the coach house!

FATHER: In her panties
                Or without her panties!
                (*Gazing out the window*) Ohh,
                Look how they're strangling that guy,
                Look how they're mashing him. . . . Now
                They're sticking him with a bayonet!

MOTHER: O ruin and conflagration!

FATHER: We'd better cover the window with something — if they
spot us, they might come in here after us.

HENRY: You degenerate old
              Flea-bitten boozer,
              And you, you rickety, old,
              Whisky-guzzling floozy. . . . I've been far too
              Lenient
              And far too patient
              With your rotgut ravings! But now
              You will know my wrath! Out! Out! Out!
                I am alone!
              Lock them in irons!

The MOTHER *and* FATHER *are taken away by the* HENCHMEN.

FATHER: Have mercy on us!

HENRY: I shall grant this marriage myself! I shall marry her, I'll get married on my own! The rest is nothing but the foulmouthed ravings of some drunken fools! Blah-blah, blah! Bring my fiancée in here at once! It's time we began discussing the details of our nuptial ceremony. But first. . . .

CHANCELLOR: But first. . . .

HENRY: But first. . . .

CHANCELLOR: But first. . . .

HENRY: But first. . . .

Summon my courtier this . . . what's his name . . . John . . . that's it . . . John, my courtier . . . I must have a few words with him . . . and with her. . . .

All exeunt.

. . . and now we'll find out if there's anything between them . . . and if there is. . . .

Enter JOHNNY.

. . . we'll settle the matter once and for all. (*To* JOHNNY) Oh, it's you, Johnny. How are you getting along?

JOHNNY: Not bad.

HENRY: Not bad, not bad and not bad with me either! Johnny,

I'm afraid we've become involved in some . . . not altogether pleasant affair. . . .

JOHNNY: I don't care. It's better than being in the army.

HENRY: What time is it?

JOHNNY: Five-thirty.

HENRY: Where did you get that watch?

JOHNNY: I bought it in Antwerp.

HENRY: What's going on there? I understand war has been declared.

JOHNNY: So I've heard.

HENRY: But you don't know for certain.

JOHNNY: Can anything be known for certain? You know, Henry, if I were you I wouldn't believe a word anyone says around here. . . . There's something false and pretentious about everything here. . . .

HENRY: You're right, Johnny, nothing is real around here. . . . Everyone pretends to be himself and lies in order to tell the truth. . . . It's even a little amusing, if you ask me. . . . But I've already got used to it. And what about yourself, Johnny . . . are you a little . . . hm . . . tight too?

JOHNNY: Me?

HENRY: Everyone around here is getting drunk on something different. And so I thought perhaps you'd been . . . drinking something too.

JOHNNY: No.

HENRY: Well, then why do you look so sad?

JOHNNY: Me? I'm not sad at all. Quite the contrary.

HENRY: (*sadly*) In appearance you aren't, but all the same you are . . . and your sadness is lurking in the shadows. . . . Hallo, hallo, come on out here, come on out here!

MOLLY *emerges from the shadows.*

What's new?

MOLLY: Nothing.

HENRY: How have you been?

MOLLY: All right.

HENRY: I have something to tell you . . . both of you. . . . You won't believe it but ever since that drunkard joined you together with the flower, ha, ha, ha, in such a peculiar position, into a statue, ha, ha, ha, I can't get rid of the impression that there's something between you two . . . that something's going on between you two . . . ha, ha, ha!

> Ha, ha, ha!
> Ha, ha, ha!
> Well, how do I know!

JOHNNY: What's that supposed to mean? That you're jealous?

HENRY: You're speaking to me, but for *whom* are you speaking?

JOHNNY: I don't understand.

HENRY: You're standing there as if you were alone — but with *whom* are you standing? (*To* MOLLY) Why don't you look at him?

MOLLY: Why should I?

HENRY: Even if you don't look at him, it's *him* you're not looking at.

MOLLY: (*theatrically*) Henry, I love you!

HENRY: Yes, you love me, and he is my friend. You love me and you're a respectable girl . . . but what have you been serving? (*To* JOHNNY) And what have you been serving?

JOHNNY: What do you mean?

HENRY: Haven't you been serving evil? You have more crimes on your conscience than a common criminal. You are both respectable people, you are both innocent, you both come from a good home . . . but what have you been serving? So now

You serve her, and let
Her serve you!

MOLLY: (*theatrically*) Oh, don't torture me like this!

HENRY: Both you and he love me . . . but only when *each of you
is alone*! But the two of you . . . but the two of you *together*. . . . Together you are altogether different from what you
are separately!

JOHNNY: The two of us together are nothing, so stop persecuting
us as well as yourself!

HENRY: Us! Us! Why do you say 'us'? Ah, what strange things
go on in this world of ours!
Imagine — after he threw away that flower, it suddenly became
apparent that you were together . . . you must have been aware of
that yourselves. . . . And now everyone is joining you together,
and I am likewise joining you together . . . in my mind, of course .
. . and you are becoming more and more intimately connected!
Oh, in some strange, inexplicable way that man has joined you
together in wedlock! He must be a priest! An unholy priest of
some mysterious rite. . . . A psychological priest!

JOHNNY: What's happening to you? You're all excited.

HENRY: Am I? I'm beginning to doubt whether I exist at all. It
seems to me that I feel, that I think, that I make decisions . . .
but in reality nothing is decided inside me; everything is
decided between . . . between ourselves. . . . It's between
ourselves that spring the forces, the charms, the gods, the
illusions which toss us about like straws in the wind. . . . And
we flounder along. . . .

JOHNNY: How so?

HENRY: Look what happened to me, for instance. He joined you
together in a certain way, stacked you one on top of the other,
multiplied you one times the other — or again, he attached you
to her and her to you — and made out of you something which
excites me . . . which intoxicates me to such an extent that
(*menacingly*) I shall not rest until I have married her. Remember that.

JOHNNY: I won't stand in your way.

HENRY: Oh, why has my nature brought me to this? Why after
such a cloudy . . . cloudy . . . voyage have I put in to such a
port? How is such a phenomenon to be explained? Perhaps
secretly I harbour a certain affection for you — an inarticulate,
illicit, amoral and abnormal affection.

JOHNNY: Whatever that's supposed to mean.

HENRY: Perhaps subconsciously I have been jealous about her all
along . . . and of you . . . and regarded you all along as my
rival?

JOHNNY: So what?

HENRY: All the same, who knows whether it is possible . . .
whether in general it is possible for a man to fall in love with a
woman without the co-operation, without the intermediary of
another man? It may be that in general man is incapable of
responding to a woman except through the intermediary of
another man. Might this not be some new form of love? Before,
only two were needed, but today it's three.

JOHNNY: I think you're exaggerating.

HENRY: Perhaps this is something which has been imposed on
me from without; perhaps deep down inside I don't feel that
way at all, but merely feel obliged to behave as though in fact I
did. My head is spinning from this winding, tortuous road
down which I keep walking, and walking . . . endlessly . . .
without a moment's rest. . . . Oh, heavy are these gates, oppressive is this ceiling, strange and enigmatic is this sky. Oh, that
drunkard has made me drunk. Oh, that priest really is a priest.
With his finger . . . with his finger . . . he has fashioned an idol
out of you . . . before which I must kneel and offer sacrifice as
in a dream.

> The hell I will!
> I am still the King! It is I who rule!
> I shall rule! Oh, Henry, Henry, Henry! I am alone!
> I shall confer this marriage myself! Henry!
> Don't let yourself be ruled! You be the one who rules!

>Henry, cast down these gods, destroy these spells
>And your own throne ascend!

How strange that sounded. Damn it! If only I didn't have to speak in such an artificial manner. And here she is . . . standing right beside us . . . and listening.

MOLLY: (*theatrically*) Why do you torture yourself and me so!

HENRY: What an insufferable ham! There are times when I'd like to. . . . (*Makes a gesture as though he is about to strike her*)

MOLLY: (*in a vulgar tone*) Hey, you needn't try any of that on me, mister!

HENRY:　Leave me.
　　　　I have to talk with him in private.
　　　　Don't go too far away though. Have
　　　　The servants bring you some tea.

　　MOLLY *goes out*.

　　　　And now
　　　　Let's get down to business. I only wish I knew the
　　　　　　outcome of all this.
　　　　What a dreadful silence. . . .
　　　　These walls and everything around here is waiting
　　　　　　patiently to hear
　　　　What I am going to say.

It's been a long time since I've felt so jumpy. (*To* JOHNNY) Ah, Johnny, how's it going?

JOHNNY:　All right.

HENRY:　I'd like to have a few words with you. Sit down.

JOHNNY:　All right.

HENRY:　　I have something unpleasant to tell you
　　　　　Something which may even be a little abnormal
　　　　　In the sense that it's not altogether common or usual
　　　　　But departs rather from the normal course of events.

JOHNNY:　　What do I care if something's abnormal
　　　　　As long as I am normal!

HENRY: The point is if I told you in an ordinary manner
It would not be convincing. Everything depends
On how we speak. That is why
I have to tell you this in a manner which is perhaps a trifle
Artificial

And I must ask you on your part not to respond to me in a normal manner, but to conduct yourself exactly as I tell you. No one will be coming in here. We'll lock the door.

JOHNNY: Do whatever you like.

HENRY: I know. You've already been forced to do so many strange things in spite of your youth. But I assure you this is not a caprice of mine, but something far more serious. As you know, my dear Johnny, I have deposed my father, the King, and ascended the throne myself. And today I have decided to grant myself a marriage to my fiancée, Princess Mary. Say: Yes, I know.

JOHNNY: Yes, I know.

HENRY: But what's the sense of marrying her, even in the most formal manner, if the whole Court believes you and she are enjoying some sort of intimate relations . . . and if I myself, rightly or wrongly, imagine that you and she. . . . Say: Yes.

JOHNNY: All right, if it'll make you happier: Yes.

HENRY: No, no, say 'yes' without any commentary. Honestly, nobody is listening to us . . . although we are listening to ourselves. . . . Say: Yes.

JOHNNY: Yes.

HENRY: Of course, it would be quite simple for me to . . . to do away with you . . . to arrest you as I did with that drunkard. I could even liquidate you, kill you, let's say. But even if I did, it wouldn't change a thing, because . . . because I would always be left with the foreboding suspicion that she really belonged to you and not to me. Say: Yes.

JOHNNY: Yes.

HENRY: These curtains are impossible. I don't understand why
this palace is so shabby and poorly kept. There are so many
servants around here and still the dirt is everywhere. I have to
do something about that. Don't say anything. I'm not finished.
What do you think of me?

JOHNNY: I think you're sick.

HENRY: I'll explain a few things to you, as far as they can be
explained.
Ever since I became involved in all this, I've been wavering
between two poles: between responsibility and irresponsibility,
between truth and falsity. On the one hand, I'm convinced that
what is going on here is unreal, irresponsible, artificial,
cheap. . . . On the other hand, I take all this very seriously and
feel as though I bear final responsibility for everything.

      I can't refrain from using artificial phrases.

But at the same time these phrases appear less artificial to me
than simplicity itself.

      I know I am not a real king.
      And yet I feel like a king.
      I'm enjoying every minute of it.

But at the very same time I know this game is not quite so
innocent as it seems. I feel as if, when I pretend something, I
actually bring that something into existence, as though with my
every word and deed I conjure up and create something . . .
something far more powerful than myself.
What do you think of that?

JOHNNY: It's pretty vague.

HENRY: Yes, but you behave at times as though you knew something about it — and so do the others. . . . What do you know?
Do you know more or less than I do? No, I haven't gone crazy.
I am a clear-thinking, modern man. Why do I really wish to
marry her? Because I'd like to have her as she was before —
and I know and I am convinced that if I possessed her without
marrying her, I would not be possessing my former fiancée but
some worn-out, broken-down slut. . . . I would like this marriage

which I'm bestowing upon myself and her to be truly sacred. Does that sound like the idea of a mystic or that of a madman? Or am I incapable of such a sacred act? In the last instance, what is really crucial here? Other people. If others acknowledge the sacredness of that act, then it will be sacred — sacred for them. If they acknowledge her as my chaste and noble Queen, then she will become a queen — for them. And if she's a queen for them, then she's a queen for me.

JOHNNY: Your ideas are sound, but you're making a funny impression on me.

HENRY: Wait a moment. I don't have the power to erase from her past . . . the fact that she was once a whore in some dive . . . and that she once kept company with a lot of drunkards. But if I force everyone, including myself, to accept this solemn marriage which at the same time will have the effect of sanctifying both my love and her honour — then it will be accepted as such. For everything is decided between people! Everything comes from people!

> And now listen
> But listen carefully: as you know, in a moment
> I shall carry out this act. . . . I am in need of strength
> But you are weakening me. . . .

JOHNNY: Aha.

HENRY: I'll explain my plan of action to you. It's an extremely simple and even dull plan.
I have given orders for everyone to attend a ball at the Royal Court. At this ball, with the help of glances, laughter, caresses, etc. . . . Molly and I will generate between ourselves the greatest amount of love possible. Between ourselves we shall create that love, purity, and fidelity . . . which once existed between us. At the very same time I shall force this pack of fools to pump me full of divinity through tokens of respect and admiration — and then I shall very calmly confer a marriage upon myself and her which will legalize and sanctify everything. . . . What's so strange about that?

> Nothing.

Nothing. But you understand that first of all I must conquer
that which is engendered between you . . . and that which
weakens me. . . . I am in need of strength.

> But you are depriving me of it. . . .
> And now I shall tell you something
> Quite unexpected: you will be obliged
> To kill yourself — and the only reason
> For that is: I command you to do it
> And it is my will. . . .

JOHNNY: What a nice proposition!

HENRY: I realize it's a little . . . silly. . . . Do you suppose I'm not
ashamed? This is horribly artificial. But I'm only saying it . . .
by way of a little experiment. . . . I'm merely curious to see
how it sounds — understand? Obviously

> You shouldn't take any of this in earnest
> Who in his right mind, after all, would take it
>   seriously!

It's just that I would like to hear the sound of my own voice,
that's all. But I'd also like to hear how what you are going to
say sounds. Therefore I'll ask you to

> Bow your head and bend your arms and legs,
>   crouch down a little
> And say: If that is your will, Henry, then yes, I'd be
>   glad to.

JOHNNY: I'm not an actor.

HENRY: Imagine you're learning a poem by heart.

JOHNNY: I don't want to imagine anything.

HENRY: Imagine you're a priest pronouncing the words to some
sort of incantation.

JOHNNY: I don't want to imagine anything.

HENRY: Don't you think that a thousand years from now people
will be speaking to one another in a completely different
fashion from the way we do today?

JOHNNY: That's very possible.

HENRY: And that their conversations will be infinitely richer? There are many melodies which our songbook of today does not contain. What harm can it possibly do you to utter these words by way of a little experiment? And to bow your head?

JOHNNY: What good will it do you if I recite them? Words are not facts.

HENRY: Of course not. No, no, don't think for a moment that I believe in any kind of magical incantations. I am a modern mind. But what harm can it do you to say that . . . and to see how you'll feel while saying it? I'd just like you to get a little taste, a little sample of yourself while you're saying it . . . so you can see what it's like. . . . To a certain extent it can even be thought of in scientific terms. Words evoke certain psychic states in us . . . they create worlds of reality between us. . . . If you said something similar to that . . . something strange . . . then I could say something even stranger and then, by mutually assisting one another, we could go on and on. So you see — it's not quite as difficult or as absurd as it seemed. Two people can do anything. And moreover

> What do you care if something's abnormal
> As long as you are normal!

JOHNNY: All right . . . if it'll make you any happier. . . .

HENRY: Wait, wait, stand right here beside me. No one can see us, right? No one can see us through the keyhole. This is just between ourselves. Damn it, it's quiet around here! It's as if there was nothing to it, but it's enough to give a person the jitters. Sit down. No, on second thoughts, stand over here, next to this chair, bow your head

> And let your arms droop. Now I'll walk over
> To you and stand here beside you and place
> My old hand on your young shoulder. It's cold in
>   here!
> Chilly, isn't it? I'm touching you. . . .

MY DEAREST JOHNNY. . . . No, no, that's quite unnecessary . . .

there's no need for any prologue. . . . YOU MUST KILL YOURSELF
BECAUSE THAT IS MY WILL. Now answer the way you were told.

JOHNNY: All right. IF THAT IS YOUR WILL, HENRY, THEN I'D BE
GLAD TO.

HENRY: BE PRESENT AT MY WEDDING AND WHEN THE TIME
COMES KILL YOURSELF WITH THIS KNIFE. (*He hands him the
knife*)

JOHNNY: VERY WELL.

HENRY: Well, what new Johnny? Tell me, are they feeding you
well at least?

JOHNNY: I can't complain.

HENRY: What time is it?

JOHNNY: Eight-thirty.

HENRY: That watch is worth at least twice the amount you paid
for it — if I remember correctly. . . .

JOHNNY: I made a good deal on it.

HENRY: It's a good-looking watch. Well, for the time being.
Goodbye.

JOHNNY: Goodbye. (*He exits*)

HENRY: (*alone*)
              A game
              Let's suppose this is a game
              But . . . what is it really? To what extent can such
                  games be dangerous?
              I would like to know the real capacity of words
              What is my own capacity?
              A dream? Yes, that's right, a dream . . . child's play. . . .

(*To a piece of furniture*) Are you looking at me? I am caught in
a network of glances, in a precinct of looks, and everything
which I am looking at is looking at me

              Even though I'm alone
              Alone

Surrounded by this silence. . . I stick out my arm.
  This ordinary
Normal
Commonplace
Gesture becomes charged with meaning because it's
  not intended
For anyone in particular. . . .
I move my fingers in the silence, and my being
Expands itself to become itself
The seed of a seed. I, I, I! I alone!
And yet if I, I, I alone am, why then
(Let's try that for effect) am I not?

What does it matter (I ask) that I, I am in the very middle, the
very centre of everything, if I, I can never be

Myself?
I alone.
I alone.

Now that you're alone, completely alone, you might at least
stop this incessant recitation

This fabrication of words
This production of gestures

But you, even when you're alone, pretend that you're alone,
and you go on

(For once now let's try to be sincere)

Pretending to be yourself
Even to your very self.

I alone
I alone (Let's emphasize that once more) . . . while
  out there
Nothing but cries, screams and blood, alas, alas, and
  fear
Oh, never before has any man had
To solve such insoluble problems
Or groan under a more awesome burden
Of pain and dishonour. . . How should I view all

this?

What attitude should I adopt? Why, why,

> In the presence of this vile, inhuman
> And disgusting world I might wrinkle my brow
> And lift my arms to heaven, I might
> Roll my hand into a fist or pass my hand
> Across my wise and thoughtful brow
> I
> Yes, that's right, I. . . . Such are the
> Attitudes I might adopt . . . in your presence
> And for your benefit! But not for my own! I'm not
> in need
> Of any attitude! I don't feel
> Other people's pain! I only recite
> My humanity! No, I do not exist
> I haven't any 'I', alas, I forge myself
> Outside myself, outside myself, alas, alas, oh, the
> hollow
> Empty orchestra of my 'alas,' you rise up from my
> void
> And sink back into the void!
>
> Oh, you demagogues!
> (Be vehement, sarcastic when you say that)
> Whose mouths are full of morality and
> Self-righteousness! (Now grimace
> Scornfully, mockingly and make a sweeping gesture
> with your hand)
> In vain are all your books and philosophies
> Articles and lectures,
> Systems and arguments,
> Definitions and observations,
> Visions, revelations and passions before
> Before this mass of two billion people
> Who are smothering each other in an eternal,
> Dark and shapeless, untamed lust. . . .
> In vain does your fly buzz about the nose
> Of that green and black abyss (Now let your laughter
> resound
> Your private and discreet

Quiet and ineffable
Humanly human laughter. . . .) While you out there
Persist in your endless posing
We go on pinching ourselves here in our own little
    way
Underneath the bushes of our destiny.

(And now, to bring
This monologue to a close)

I reject every order, every concept
I distrust every abstraction, every doctrine
I don't believe in God or in Reason!
Enough of these gods! Give me man!
May he be like me, troubled and immature
Confused and incomplete, dark and obscure
So I can dance with him! Play with him! Fight with
    him!
Pretend to him! Ingratiate myself with him!
And rape him, love him and forge myself
Anew from him, so I can grow through him, and in
    that way
Celebrate my marriage in the sacred human church!

From all sides enter the DIGNITARIES, LADIES, CHANCELLOR,
CHIEF OF POLICE. *Music, ball.*

CHORUS: The quadrille has begun, let every voice ring!
              Long live His Majesty, His Majesty the King!

HENRY: The quadrille has begun, let every voice ring!

CHANCELLOR:
              Long live His Majesty, His Majesty the King!

HENRY: (*strolling arm in arm with the* CHANCELLOR)
              Look, my good fellow, look how they dance!
              Lulled by the chorus into a wondrous trance
              Oh, the sweet perfume that dreams engender
              Oh, 'tis a night of golden-haired splendour. . . .

CHANCELLOR:
              This quadrille is stately in the extreme

> It helps to sweeten our every dream
> The soul takes wing, it leaves no tracks
> Its hair is as golden as newly spun flax!

HENRY: Though the sense be lacking, let rhyme abound
The sweet smoke of hopes vain and unsound
Let rhythm and rhyme spin merrily 'round
In an unending circle as far as Capetown!

Pooh! Pooh! Pooh!
That's enough! Stop!

The GUESTS *stop dancing.*

Tell them to bow!

They do so.

Once more!

They bow again.

Once more!

They bow again.

These bows are inflating me. . . . Where are my men? (*The* HENCHMEN *come in*) I swear they are a frightful lot, amen. Where is the Chief of Police? (CHIEF *comes forward*) You and your men are to grab everything and everybody by the snout, amen. If anyone so much as dares to . . . lay a finger on me . . . pounce on him at once. Now then. (*Walking among the* GUESTS *and scrutinizing them*) Is everybody here? That old battle-axe — who is she?

CHANCELLOR: That's Princess Pirulu.

HENRY: I knew she was a princess the moment I laid eyes on her — she's so vulgar-looking. And that moron?

CHANCELLOR: He's a supreme moron.

HENRY: There's a moronic look in his eye. And who's that flabby, sweaty-looking character with the potbelly and the white skin?

CHANCELLOR: A gourmet.

HENRY: He has a pimple behind his ear. What exactly does he taste?

CHANCELLOR: His own distaste.

HENRY: Good. I see you've brought me the cream of the crop. (*To a* HENCHMAN, *pointing to the* GOURMET) Step on his foot — but good and hard so it hurts.

Quiet

It's quiet here, isn't it? (*Glancing around the room*) The very elite, indeed. It's quite evident they represent the highest circles of this illustrious kingdom. But why are they all so old? This is a congress of old duffers!

CHANCELLOR: I beg your pardon, Sire.

HENRY: But these are not people! These are caricatures! Just look at all these spectacles, goatees and moustaches — how it disgusts me to look at all these shrivelled-up emaciated bodies — these pitiful, sclerotic and despondend varicose veins, fallen arches, sagging breasts, protruding bellies, false teeth, this inertia, sclerosis, atrophy, these infirmities and maladies, defects and blemishes, and all this hideous, shameful naked-ness! And moreover how distinguished they look, coddled, pampered and fawned upon by the most chic hairdressers! Hey, corpse, show me your sock: goodness but that's an exquisite sock, such a tasteful colour and made of the finest silk too — what an elegant piece of hose! Only your foot is in a state of decomposition. These are people already in the process of disintegrating. They have a cemetery look about them. And these are the people who govern?

GUESTS: (*dancing*)
           The quadrille has begun, let every voice ring!
           Long live His Majesty, His Majesty the King!

They stop dancing. Enter the LACKEYS *with trays loaded down with bottles.*

LACKEYS: Burgundy, Tokay, Malaga, port!

HENRY: (*without taking his eyes off the* GUESTS) What a revelry

of faces! What a debauchery of noses and bellies! What an orgy
of baldness!

> Orchestra of unbridled ugliness
> Some music for my wedding! This licentiousness
>   suits my purpose.

LACKEYS: Burgurdy, Tokay, Malaga, port!

HENRY: Where is my fiancée?

CHANCELLOR: Here she comes now with those maidens dressed
all in white.

HENRY: Let her approach and let her smile at me and lower her
eyes as she bows before me. I shall bow and taking her gently
by the shoulders I shall prevent her from kneeling down, at the
same time I shall smile at her the way I used to do in former
times. (*He and* MOLLY *do so*)

CHANCELLOR: (*aside*) Your Majesty, everyone is listening.

HENRY: (*loudly*) That's precisely what I want them to do. We
don't love one another — we merely engender the feeling of
love between us. . . . (*To* MOLLY) Why aren't you smiling?
Smile at me, the way you did before you were raped and
became a slut for some innkeeper, understand? Otherwise, I'll
let you have it. And don't look around — don't try to catch
anyone else's glance — you know I'm jealous of Johnny. (*To
the* CHANCELLOR) I'm deliberately saying all this out loud
because there's no need to conceal anything here; here everything is in the open. Look how graciously she's smiling. That
smile evokes within me a multitude of memories and moves
me in the presence . . . in the presence of all these people. . . .

> My darling, if only your smile
> Would reverberate off them and come back to me
> In waves a hundred times stronger. . . .
> Trust in me, have no fear, I shall find a way
> To fill the void of my heart
> And I shall love you again, as
> I loved you once before

Let her squeeze my hand in secret. All right. Now what? What

should we do now, Chamberlain, to make this a truly royal
reception.

CHAMBERLAIN: (*announces*)
                Circle.
                Circle.
                Circle.

LACKEYS: Port!

The GUESTS *group themselves into small circles.*

CHAMBERLAIN: With your leave, Sire, with your leave, Sire, with
your leave, Sire the most illustrious names, the greatest for-
tunes, the highest offices, the very flower, the very elite, the
very cream, in short, Your Majesty, everyone — dreams of
nothing else save the honour to kiss your hand, Sire. I have the
honour! I have the honour! I have the honour to present to His
Majesty our renowned poet Paul Valery, the undisputed pride
and glory of mankind . . . and the poet Rainer Maria Rilke,
likewise the pride and glory of mankind. Men of genius!
Immortal! Incomparable!

HENRY: Let them pay homage to me. (*To* MOLLY) Take my arm.
Why are those old ladies bowing to one another and not to me?
I'm going to blow myself up and squish out their guts!

                Who gave any of you permission to clown around?
                There'll be no fooling around in my presence!

CHAMBERLAIN: One moment, Your Majesty, forgive me, Your
Majesty. . . . Before rendering homage to you, they must first of
all affirm their own greatness by bowing before each other.

HENRY: This one must be having trouble with his kidneys! What
do you mean they must bow before each other?

CHAMBERLAIN: It's just that the greatness and profundity of
these two unrivalled poets cannot be fully appreciated by
anybody except themselves. Since all the others are lesser
poets, they are equally incompetent to judge or appreciate or
understand them. Therefore by exchanging bows with each
other they are testifying to one another's greatness, which they
will then place at His Majesty's feet.

The POETS *bow before* HENRY.

CHANCELLOR: Oh, heaven help us. . . .

HENRY: Good. The glory of these two melancholy lute players is now a part of me. Keep on pumping. Who's that longhaired imbecile over there?

CHAMBERLAIN: A pianist.

HENRY: Why are all those senile old biddies squirming around over there goggle-eyed, madly clutching their shrivelled-up breasts?

CHAMBERLAIN: Women always go into convulsions in the company of an actor, singer, or virtuoso.

HENRY: These are just the sort of second-rate gods I need. Tell this guy to pump his divinity into me with a bow. He hasn't got much longer to live anyway — he's a consumptive. Just look at those delicate fingers. And this old hag? Why is the scullion arranging a kneeling rail in front of her?

CHANCELLOR: Oh, heaven help us. . . .

CHAMBERLAIN: With your leave, Sire . . . forgive me, Sire, it's just that the Princess, as Your Majesty has already been pleased to remark, is a rather vulgar woman. She would give anything to fall down on her knees before Your Majesty, but her knees are. . . .

HENRY: (*lifting up her skirt*) Hm . . . as a matter of fact . . . she is a little on the dumpy side. . . .

CHAMBERLAIN: Yes, but she has a servant girl and this servant girl will render her knees honourable before they render homage to Your Majesty.

HENRY: To tell you the truth, I would prefer the knees of this young wench.

A LACKEY: (*pouring the wine*) Burgundy!

CHAMBERLAIN: No, that's impossible! She's this woman's servant.

CHANCELLOR: Her servant. At her service!

HENRY: (*to a* LADY) What's your name?

LADY: Gertrude.

HENRY: What are you dying from, excuse me, I mean, what are you living on?

LADY: A pension.

HENRY: What do you occupy yourself with?

LADY: My feeble condition.

HENRY: What are you living for?

LADY: To enjoy everybody's respect.

HENRY: This woman is a goddess. An altar adorned with precious jewels and perfumed by the servant girl. Let her kneel down before me on this kneeling rail and let her servant kiss her on the heel. Now start pumping! Oh, how I'm itching! Damn this itching — Chamberlain, scratch me just above my left shoulder blade.

CHAMBERLAIN: Here?

HENRY: No, higher, to the left.

CHAMBERLAIN: Here?

HENRY: No, to the right. Oh, what's the difference. But it annoys me. . . .

CHAMBERLAIN: (*in a confidential manner*) It annoys you?

CHANCELLOR: (*curious*) Does it annoy you?

HENRY: It's nothing, nothing at all. It's even amusing. Where is my father? Show my ex-father in here along with my late mother. We're going to begin right away. (*To* MOLLY) Squeeze my fingers and I'll squeeze yours. . . . But the place is so empty. It seems as if there's nobody here.

> I am alone
> Together with you. . . .

MOLLY: I love you. . . .

HENRY: That's right, say that, say that out loud so everybody, everybody, everybody can hear. (*To the* CHANCELLOR) Where is my father? Show that drunkard in too!

CHANCELLOR: (*in a perfunctory manner*) Your father will be here soon.

HENRY: (*in a perfunctory manner*) Why isn't my father here?

CHANCELLOR: (*as above*) He'll be here soon.

HENRY: (*as above*) If he's going to be here, let him be here.

CHANCELLOR: (*as above*) Soon it will be that your father will be here.

The FATHER *and* MOTHER *along with the* DRUNKARD *are carried in by the* HENCHMEN *and thrown at* HENRY'*s feet.*

HENRY: Now what?

CHANCELLOR: Nothing.

CHIEF: Nothing.

HENRY: Nothing.

　　　　　The same bunch I knelt before a little while ago.

He nudges his parents with his foot.

　　　　　I don't know. . . .
　　　　　I could eat something. . . .

FATHER: I could eat something too.

MOTHER: So could I.

HENRY: For the time being though there isn't anything to eat.

MOTHER: Well, if there isn't anything, there isn't anything.

FATHER: Do you remember, Henry, how we used to go for drives in the country together in the wagon?

MOLLY: And I sometimes went along too when the weather was nice.

HENRY: It's true — we had some pleasant outings together. . . .
(*He stands up*) But that's beside the point. Completely beside
the point! This is not the time for chit-chat. . . . I have to grant
myself a marriage!

CHANCELLOR: Grant yourself a marriage!

HENRY: Burgundy!

A LACKEY: Burgundy!

HENRY: Burgundy!
              Hey, Chamberlain, let's empty this goblet
              In honour of my lady!

CHAMBERLAIN: Burgundy!

CHANCELLOR: Burgundy!

A LACKEY: Burgundy!

HENRY: To the health
              Of my loyal subjects!

GUESTS: (*raising their goblets*)
              Long live His Majesty the King!

LACKEYS: (*raising their wine trays*)
              Burgundy! Burgundy! Burgundy!

GUESTS: (*dancing*)
              The quadrille has begun, let every voice ring!
              Long live His Majesty, His Majesty the King!
              Under the spell of this enchanting wine
              May the spell of this ball reach limits sublime!

HENRY: (*strolling with* MOLLY)
              O 'tis a night of magical splendours
              Illusory is the power that love engenders
              The dreamlike waft of eternal illusions
              And the melancholy music of nostalgic allusions!

MOLLY: Oh, the tears I once shed for my maidenly dreams
              A petal adrift on a sea of timid sighs
              The lilacs of the past are in bloom again it seems

> And the brother I feared lost is standing before my
> eyes.

HENRY: Look how gracefully they dance the quadrille!
It's a dance that's designed to give a man a thrill
And instruct the human heart in love and good will
Enough! Enough! Stop!
(*To a* LACKEY) Burgundy!

A LACKEY: Burgundy!

HENRY: Burgundy!

A LACKEY: Burgundy!

HENRY: (*advancing toward the crowd*)
Get out of my way!
Move back! I'm advancing
Toward you! This is my person!
It is I, I alone! Space!
Let there be space! It is I who am here!
Here, in the very centre of everything!
And now watch carefully!

Move one of those empty chairs over here, And have her sit
down on it.
Now I'll walk up to her and . . . and then what? And then I'll
touch her, for example. I'll touch her with this finger . . . and that
will mean we are married and that henceforth she is my legiti-
mate, legal, faithful, chaste, and innocent spouse. I don't need
any other ceremonies. I can invent my own ceremonies. And as
soon as I touch her, you are to fall down on your knees and by the
very fact of kneeling down you will elevate my touch to the level
of a holiness most holy . . . to the level of a nuptial ceremony. . . .
Do you dare not to go down on your knees? Do you dare not to
consecrate this marriage by kneeling down? Now on with it, on
with it, come on, let's go, let's go, oh Henry, Henry, Henry!

COURT: Henry, Henry, Henry!
On with it! On with it! Oh, Henry, Henry, Henry!

HENRY: I don't give a damn
What any of you may be thinking! But . . . what are

you thinking?
Do you think that . . . that what? (*To a* LADY) What
are you thinking?

LADY: I'm not thinking anything.

HENRY: Yes, you are, you're thinking and that goes for the rest of
you too.

A LACKEY: Port!

CHANCELLOR: They're thinking.

CHIEF: They're thinking . . . everyone is thinking. . . .

HENRY: (*thoughtfully*) They're thinking. . . . (*He goes from guest
to guest, looking each in the face; he bumps into* JOHNNY) Oh,
Johnny, how are you?

JOHNNY: All right.

HENRY: What's new?

JOHNNY: Not much.

HENRY: Good. (*They remain standing opposite one another*)

CHANCELLOR:

His Majesty
Seems curiously absorbed. . . .

CHIEF: Yes, the King is absorbed. . . .

HENRY: (*to himself*)

I don't want to drink any more. . . .
I'm not going to drink any more. . . .
(*To everyone*)
And you perhaps thinking
That I am able to rule here solely because
They are shackled. . . . That I could not
Stand up to them if they were released?. . .
(*To the* CHANCELLOR)
So be it then!
Untie these prisoners and let them attack
Me!

CHANCELLOR: Sire!

CHIEF: Sire!

HENRY: (*to* JOHNNY)
> You know
> What's expected of you!
> (*Aloud*)
> Come on! Untie them! Let's make it clear
> Once and for all who is in command here!

The MOTHER *and* FATHER *stand up. Now for the first time it is possible to see the frightful state this couple is in as their bloody, swollen faces gradually become visible.*

HENRY: What buffoonery!
> Oh, how frightfully artificial! All the same, this
>   artificiality
> Is frightful!

CHANCELLOR: They look as though they just got out of prison.

HENRY: Are you trying to frighten me?
> Why don't you go ahead and attack me?
> Nothing?

CHANCELLOR: Nothing.

CHIEF: Nothing.

DIGNITARY/TRAITOR: Nothing.

A group of TRAITORS *approaches with evil intentions.*

HENRY: Henchmen, get over here!

The HENCHMEN *come over and stand directly behind him.*

> If they attack
> Me, you attack them. . . . But
> Why don't they attack?

CHANCELLOR: Nothing.

CHIEF: Nothing.

DIGNITARY/TRAITOR: Nothing.

CHAMBERLAIN: Nothing.

HENRY: I am not ashamed
              I don't feel any pity for you
              Nor am I afraid of you
              No, no . . . I merely have to back down from them
              As though I were afraid, as though I were
                  ashamed. . .
              I wonder what they're up to.

CHANCELLOR: Nothing.

CHIEF: Nothing.

CHAMBERLAIN: Nothing.

HENRY: Ohhh, here they come!
              What do you want? What do you want?

He runs up to the FATHER, *but does not dare touch him.*

              You pig!

DRUNKARD: (*violently, off to one side*) You pig!

HENRY: (*To the* DRUNKARD) You pig!

HENRY *and the* DRUNKARD *come down to the front of the stage.*

DRUNKARD: Pig!
              You piggish pigmonger pig of a slut
              Hoggish boar of a greasy porker!

HENRY: Sow of a souse!

DRUNKARD: Prick of a pig!

HENRY: Swine!

FATHER: Oh, what a pigsty, what a pigsty!

LACKEYS: Oh, Burgundy, Burgundy, Burgundy!

DRUNKARD: Piggish pig!
              Your girl friend is a slut of a sow! Oink! Oink! Oink!

HENRY: You're a pig yourself!
              You pig, pig, pig!

LACKEYS:	Oh, Burgundy, Burgundy, Burgundy!
HENRY:	Idiot You're an idiot!
DRUNKARD:	You're the one who's an idiot, You idiot! You dried-up tit of a sow!
HENRY:	Pig puss!
DRUNKARD:	You're a pig! A piggified pig! A piggish, piggicized, piggerized superpig! Piggy-wiggy! Oink! Oink! Oink!
HENRY:	Pig!
MOTHER:	He's grunting like a hog!
CHIEF:	He's drooling like a dog!
FATHER:	Oh, what swine, oh, what swine!
LACKEYS:	Oh, what wine, oh, what wine!
HENRY:	You boar Just try and touch me!
DRUNKARD:	And I will toushh you I'll toushh you yet, I'll toushh you yet And then I'll blow myself up and blow this pig down, Squish out his guts and spit all over him! Isn't that right Miss Molly?

Quiet.

Do you see this Finger?

HENRY:	Say whatever you please I'm not afraid. . .
DRUNKARD:	Fellow citizens!

I ain't no educated man, but I got eyes . . . and I see they mean to have a pretty posh wedding. . . . But what I keep wonderin' is — how can they go through with it, with the wedding I mean, when the bride has already been . . . ahem . . . married to someone else?

Do you see this Finger?
Look at my Finger!
Don't look at anything else but my Finger!

HENRY: But it's tickling me!

DRUNKARD: Don't look at anything else but my Finger!

HENRY: I've got goose pimples
All over me....

DRUNKARD: Look carefully at my Finger. Look in which direction of the room it's pointing....

HENRY: I feel like laughing....

DRUNKARD: Look at how my Finger's pointing at something over there behind those Personages.... There's a young man over there.... Look how I'm pointing with my Finger in his direction.... In a second the shame of this royal family will be made public....

HENRY: This display
Is shamelessly
Touching my Person....

DRUNKARD: (*shouting*)
The King is a cuckold
His fiancée has been carrying on behind his back!
Step aside
And you will see the fellow
Who's been playing footsie with her!
There he is, in back of the guests!

The GUESTS *make way, revealing* JOHNNY'S CORPSE.

CHANCELLOR: Dead.

CHIEF: Murdered.

FATHER: A corpse.

MOTHER: Dead.

CHAMBERLAIN: A corpse.

DRUNKARD: (*startled*)
A corpse!
I'll be d.... Stabbed with a knife....
Who stabbed him?

A GUEST: (*to* HENRY)
Sire!
He stabbed himself!

DRUNKARD: He killed himself? But why?

HENRY: On my orders...

ALL: The King, the King!

HENRY: But ... is this for real?
(*A moment later*)
Put something under his head.

ALL: The King, the King!

HENRY: Who would ever have believed it? It's only a dream. It's even extremely artificial. And yet he's lying here

And she is standing over there
And here am I.
(*A moment later*)
Now I can grant myself a marriage!

ALL: The King, the King, oh, Henry, Henry, Henry!

LACKEYS: O Burgundy, Burgundy, Burgundy!

HENRY: Who would have ever believed it? It's nothing but a dream. The whole thing is even extremely artificial. And yet he's lying there

And she is standing over there

(*Lowering his voice*) I'll walk over to her now and make out of her what I damn well please.... I'm going to take her and marry her ... with all my power....

But what was it I wanted to say?

There was something I wanted to say, but now I've forgotten what it was.

Let's see, what was it?. . . Oh, yes! It seems there isn't going to
be any marriage because. . . .

> I don't feel like it any more
> (*To* MOLLY) I'm sorry. . . .

CHANCELLOR: (*upstage, bent over* JOHNNY) He's got bloodstains
all over his shirt. . . .

FATHER: Well, no one can bring him back to life now.

MOTHER: He must have been insane! At first I thought it was just
a joke . . . but when I saw the way he was lying on the
ground. . . .

DRUNKARD: There's no point in talking about it any more. . . .
He's done for. Finished.

HENRY: Oh, I know perfectly well it isn't true!
> And yet. . . .
> Ladies
> And gentlemen
> Kneel down and bow your heads
> Because instead of a wedding . . . there's going to

be a   funeral!

CHANCELLOR: A funeral.

FATHER: Well, if there's got to be a funeral, there's got to be one,
I suppose.

HENRY: Lay him down over here. (*To* MOLLY) You stand
> over here beside him.
> This corpse is my creation
> But this creation is incomprehensible
> Dark
> Obscure. . . .
> More powerful than I, and
> Perhaps not even my own!
> Form a funeral procession!

CHANCELLOR: It's a funeral march!

FATHER: It's a funeral march!

HENRY: No! I'm not responsible for anything here!
I don't understand my own words!
I have no control over my own deeds!
I know nothing, nothing, nothing, I understand
    nothing, nothing, nothing!
Whoever says he understands is a liar!
You don't know anything
Any more than I do!

Being mutually united, we are forever arranging ourselves into new forms
And these forms well up from below. What a peculiar haze! An inexplicable melody! A delirious dance!
An ambiguous march!

    And an earthly human church
    Whose priest I am!

DRUNKARD: Whose priest I am. . . .

FATHER: (*tenderly*) Henry. . . .

MOTHER: (*tenderly*) Henry. . . .

HENRY: I am innocent.

I declare that I am as innocent as a child, that I have done nothing, that I am ignorant of everything. . . .

    No one is responsible for anything here!
    There is no such thing as responsibility!

If however, there is a corpse, then there has to be a funeral, then four of you must stand next to him so you can raise him up at a signal from me. . . .

    No, there is no responsibility
    Still, there are formalities
    To be attended to. . . .

Four of the DIGNITARIES *come over and stand next to* JOHNNY'S CORPSE.

If, however, four of you are standing over there, next to him, then four of you must stand over here, next to me.

He and I.... Four and four.... On this side and on that side....

MOTHER: My child, don't get yourself all upset, never mind about all this, Henry darling, I'm your mother after all. Can't you talk normally any more? Can't you give me a simple kiss?

HENRY: No. Nobody can speak to anybody in a normal
                manner.
            In vain do you struggle to get free of yourself in
                order to reach me, and
            In vain do I struggle to get free of myself to reach
                all of you

            Yes, I'm imprisoned....
            I am a prisoner
            Even though I am innocent.... What was it I
wanted
                to say?
            While I am standing here
            And speaking....
            Let your hands....
            Touch . . . me....

The GUARDS *who are standing behind him place their hands on his shoulders.*

            Wait a minute.
            I'm not through yet.

If I am imprisoned here, then somewhere, somewhere far away, let this deed of mine be raised on high.

They lift up JOHNNY'S CORPSE.

            And now let this funeral march of yours
            Carry you away!

Procession.

OPERETTA

Translated by Louis Iribarne

Witold Gombrowicz' last play, *Operetta*, is a witty parody of the operetta form that combines the theme of personal identity explored in his previous plays with a juxtaposition of both a capitalist and a Marxist society, making hilarious fun of both. Despite the play's basic seriousness of intent, it has a beautifully light touch and all the sparkle, glamour and glitter associated with the best Viennese operettas: and these qualities make it delightfully entertaining to read.

The plot is involved, as in all operettas. Count Charmant, a young aristocrat, plans the seduction of a girl at Prince Himalay's ball. This girl, Albertine, is attracted by nudity: But Charmant wants to give her expensive clothes. Count Hufnagel, an undercover Marxist, offers his advice on the styling of her clothes with the hidden aim of inspiring a revolution among the lackeys at the ball. On the night of the ball, Charmant and his rival, Firulet, quarrel over Albertine and fight a duel. In the ensuing chaos, the lackeys and pickpockets run amok and Hufnagel leads them into revolution. After several years' search, during which the revolutionary regime has been firmly established, Charmant and Firulet find Albertine in the hands of the pickpockets, who adore her nudity.

Commentary

The text of a modern play is becoming less and less suitable for reading. It is becoming increasingly like a musical score that comes to life only on the stage, in its production, in its performance.

But *Operetta* is difficult to read for still another reason. I have always been captivated by the form of the operetta which, in my opinion, is one of the most felicitous forms ever produced by the theatre. While opera remains something awkward, something hopelessly doomed to pretentiousness, operetta, in its divine idiocy, in its heavenly sclerosis, in its glorious etherealness thanks to song, dance, gesture and mask, seems to me the perfect theatre, perfectly theatrical. No wonder then that I finally yielded to temptation. . . .

But . . . how to fill the puppet-show void of the operetta with real drama? For, as we know, the task of the artist lies in the eternal reconciliation of contradictions, and if I have applied myself to so frivolous a form it was to furnish and replenish it with gravity and suffering. On the one hand, therefore, this operetta should, from beginning to end, be nothing but an operetta, sovereign and inviolable in its operetta-like elements; on the other hand, it should be a solemn drama of humanity. No one can imagine how much effort the dramatic organization of this nonsense cost me. To infuse an operetta with a certain passion, a certain drama, a certain pathos, without infringing upon its sacred folly — that is no small problem!

The monumental idiocy of the operetta going hand in hand with the monumental pathos of history — an operetta mask concealing the bloody visage of mankind, contorted by a ridiculous pain — would doubtless be the best way of staging *Operetta* in the theatre. And in the reader's imagination as well.

Plot

ACT ONE — Before the First World War, around 1910.

A jaded rake and a debauchee, Count Charmant, son of Prince Himalay, is planning the seduction of Albertine, a marvel of a lass. But how to make Albertine's acquaintance 'without having been introduced to her'? Charmant has devised the following scheme: a pickpocket, a young scamp and a rogue who has been engaged especially for the purpose, will sneak up to Albertine while she is asleep on a park bench and will filch something from her — a purse, a locket. . . . Charmant will then nab the pickpocket and without violating the rules of savoir-faire introduce himself to this marvel of a lass.

But what's this?! In her sleep Albertine has felt the pickpocket's hand and dreams not of a thief's but of a lover's touch . . . which is aimed not at her locket, but at her body. Henceforth, excited and enthralled, this girl will dream of nudity . . . and will lapse into sleep in order that she may once again experience that denuding touch. . . .

Damnation! For Charmant, a count dressed from head to foot, is ashamed of nudity. He adores clothes! And he is relying not on his nakedness to seduce Albertine, but on the elegance of his manners, of his suits! He does not wish to undress her but, on the contrary, to dress her — at the most expensive couturiers, at the fanciest milliners!

But who should arrive from Paris on a visit to the Himalay Castle?

None other than the celebrated Fior himself, the universal dictator of men's and women's fashion. A grand ball is scheduled to be held at the castle, with a fashion show during which the master will launch his latest creations. Thus, while Albertine dreams of nudity, Clothes, Fashion and Chic begin to reign supreme under Fior's command!

But the master is seized with anxiety and uncertainty: what sort of fashion should he decree, what sort of style should he launch if the Times are obscure, decadent, ominous, and no one knows the course of History?

Hufnagel, a count and a horse lover, offers him his advice. Let's invite the guests to collaborate, he says. Let's make it a masquerade ball and make those who wish to take part in the fashion contest put on sacks over their garments of the future which they themselves have designed. At a given signal the sacks will fall, the jury will award prizes for the best creations, and Master Fior, enriched by these ideas, will decree the fashion for the years to come.

Damnation! For Hufnagel is neither Hufnagel, nor a count, nor a horse lover! No, he is Joseph, the Prince's former valet who, after having been dismissed in the past, has now become an agitator and revolutionary agent! Ha, ha, ha! Brought into the castle under a fictitious name by the Marxist Professor, this terrorist in disguise is seeking, under the pretext of a Masked Ball, to smuggle into the castle a bloodier Fashion, a more terrifying Style . . . he wishes to sow rebellion among the Lackeys who until now have been polishing and waxing shoes. . . . He wants a Revolution.

ACT TWO — The ball at the Himalay Castle.

The guests who are going to compete for the New Fashion arrive in their sacks.

Charmant brings Albertine. Weighed down with clothes (for Charmant, instead of undressing her, dresses her) and still under the spell of the pickpocket's touch, she continually falls asleep . . . and dreams of nakedness . . . and even calls out in her sleep to nakedness. . . .

This drives Charmant and his rival Firulet insane. Charmant has come to the ball with his pickpocket on a leash. . . . To keep an eye on him? To keep him out of mischief? Or is he perhaps jealous of the pickpocket's uninhibited touch, titillated and excited by the thought that the pickpocket can get into everything with his thievish fingers?. . .

His rival, Firulet, also has a pickpocket on a leash.

Incapable of responding to Albertine's sleepy appeal Charmant and Firulet begin mocking one another, and a tragic desire for self-destruction drives them to a duel. Finally, when the Ball has unfolded itself in all the splendour of its costumes and masks, the desperate rivals unleash their pickpockets: let them do as they please, let them steal, let them poke into everything!. . .

Mayhem. Panic. The pickpockets steal at random while the guests, not knowing who is touching and tickling them, begin to squeal and go wild! Amid the general breakdown of manners and the disarray of costumes, Hufnagel, the horse lover and terrorist, gallops forth at the head of the Lackeys. . . . Revolution!

ACT THREE — The Ruins of the Himalay Castle.

Revolution.

The wind of History. . . . Quite a long time has passed. It is now after both world wars and the revolution.

Man's clothing has gone berserk. . . . In the wind, amid flashes of lightning, the weirdest disguises become visible: the prince as a lamp, the priest as a woman, a Nazi uniform, a gas mask. . . . Everyone is hiding; no one knows who anybody is. . . .

Hufnagel the rider, leading a squadron of Lackeys, gallops about in pursuit of the fascists and the bourgeois.

Meanwhile Master Fior, in a state of shock and bewilderment, tries to get his bearings somehow at this new Fashion Show.

The fascists who have been caught are then put on trial. In vain are Fior's demands for a normal legal procedure. Storm! Storm! A violent, gusty wind. . . .

But what's this?! What's this?! Charmant and Firulet come in chasing butterflies, followed by a coffin carried by two gravediggers. They relate their tale of woe: during the ball Albertine disappeared, and all that was found were the numerous remnants of her wardrobe! The pickpockets likewise vanished. Convinced therefore that Albertine had been stripped of her clothes, raped and murdered, they have set out into the world with their coffin in order to bury the naked body of Albertine.

At this point they all deposit their own defeats and sufferings in the coffin. But what's this?! What's this?! When at last Fior, denouncing man's Clothing and Fashion and Masks, with a gesture of supreme despair places in the coffin the sacred, ordinary, eternally elusive

Nudity of man . . . who should rise up out of the coffin but the naked Albertine!

How did she get into the coffin? Who hid here there?

The gravediggers throw off their masks: it's the pickpockets! It was they who kidnapped Albertine at the ball, disrobed her and hid her in the coffin. . .

O nudity eternally youthful, O youth eternally nude, O nudity eternally youthful, O youth eternally nude.

Remarks about the Acting and Staging of the Play

Music, songs, dances, scenic decorations and costumes in the classic style of the old Viennese operetta. Simple, old-fashioned melodies. . . .

But gradually *Operetta* gets caught up in the whirlwind of History and grows in madness.

The storm effects — gusts of wind, thunder — though rather rhetorical at the beginning, in the second and particularly in the third act, turn into a real storm. The Shakespearean scenes of the third act should be solemn and tragic.

The opposition clothing-nakedness is the underlying motif of *Operetta*. A dream about the nakedness of man imprisoned in the most bizarre, the most atrocious clothing. . . .

Witold Gombrowicz
Translated by Louis Iribarne

Translator's Note

In the original Count Charmant, Baron Firulet, and Prince and Princess Himalay pronounce their 'r's' as 'h's' in an affected manner character-istic of the aristocracy; hence 'deah Masteh Fioh', instead of 'dear Master Fior', 'chahmee' instead of 'charmee', etc. It has been left to the discretion of directors and actors to adopt a similar style of speech for these roles and to apply it consistently throughout the play.

Operetta was presented in February, 1970, at the Théâtre National Populaire in Paris. The cast was as follows:

MASTER FIOR	Alain Mottet
PRINCE HIMALAY	Georges Riquier
PRINCESS HIMALAY	Judith Magre
COUNT CHARMANT	Gabriel Cattand
BARON FIRULET	Guy Michel
ALBERTINE	Catherine Hubeau
THE GENERAL	Francois Maistre
ALBERTINE'S FATHER	Jacques David
ALBERTINE'S MOTHER	Francoise Bertin
THE COUNT'S PICKPOCKET	Jean-Jacques Ruysdale
THE BARON'S PICKPOCKET	Christian Baltauss
THE PRIEST	Herve Sand
THE BANKER	Bruno Balp
THE MARCHIONESS	Catherine Rethi
THE PROFESSOR	Roland Bertin
COUNT HUFNAGEL	Jacques Seiler
LORDS	Erik Kruger
	Gerard Thirion
	Alain Duverry
	Michel Chaineaud
LADISLAUS	Jean Turlier
STANISLAUS	Jean-Pierre Bagot
THE PRIEST'S HOUSEKEEPER	Annick Fougery
THE GENERAL'S ORDERLY	Etienne Dirand
THE PRINCE'S VALET	Christian Fioravanti
THE PRINCESS'S VALET	Christian Pelissier
THE BANKER'S VALET	Jean-Claude Sachot
A BEGGAR	Jean Laugier
GROOM	Jean-Paul Tribout
THE BALL GUESTS	Francoise Armel
	Daniele Barraud
	Paul Cassan
	Sandra Drai
	Mireille Piris
	Maria Salerno
	Anny Weinberger

The play was directed by Georges Wilson.

ACT ONE

A church square. Trees, benches, a promenade. In the foreground, to one side, a group of LADIES *and* GENTLEMEN: *a* BANKER, *a* GENERAL, *a* PROFESSOR, *a* MARCHIONESS. *Costumes dating back to before 1914, lavish: uniforms, frock coats, top hats, whiskers, stiff collars, canes, galloons, etc. Refined manners: bows, smiles, compliments, etc. In the background, to the left, a group of* LACK-EYS. *Four of them, in livery, with lackey faces. Out from behind the church comes* COUNT CHARMANT HIMALAY, *a golden-boy, thirty-five, a jaded rake and a fop: frock coat, top hat, gloves, cane, monocle. Behind him is his lackey* LADISLAUS.

LADIES AND GENTLEMEN: (*song, piano*)
  Oh, the count, the count, Count Charmant
  Oh, Count Charmant!

CHARMANT:
  Oh, the count, the count, Count Charmant
  Oh, Count Charmant!

Frozen, in an affected pose; to LADISLAUS.

Ladislaus, straighten my left pant leg and scratch my right shoulder-blade. Will she be coming out soon?

LADISLAUS: (*fifty, side-whiskers, in livery*) At your service, Count. (*Scratches him and straightens his pant leg*) No, Yer Grace, not yet, but won't be long now'n she'll be comin' out, Yer Grace. . . .

CHARMANT: And that pickpocket?

LADISLAUS: I've got 'im behind the bush, Yer Grace.

CHARMANT: Bring him out here so I can have a look at him.
  (LADISLAUS *leads the* PICKPOCKET *out from behind the bush:*

eighteen years old, barefoot, slender, a street urchin, scamp, hooligan) H'm, not bad. Knows his business, I suppose. . . .

LADISLAUS: Ohhh!. . . He's got a police record, Yer Grace. . . . A real pro.

CHARMANT: Hide him behind the bush and let him wait. I won't get anywhere without him. (LADISLAUS *hides the* PICKPOCKET) How many women have I bagged so far?

LADISLAUS: As of today Yer Grace has 257 and Baron Firulet has 256.

LADIES AND GENTLEMEN: (*rousing themselves*)
Oh, the count, the count, Count Charmant!
Oh, oh, Baron Firulet!

CHARMANT: That preposterous baron! Give me a mint. I have heartburn. All those oysters yesterday, champagne, poulard, ha, ha, Leontine, cette enchantesse, mimosas, orchids, jewellery and cockatoo, but afterwards what a streak of bad luck, déveine, parole d'honneur, that game of baccarat in the club, 13,575 plus 12,830, which makes a total of around 26,000, ha, ha, I gambled it all away, what a night . . . gypsies . . . I feel like taking a nap. (*Yawns*) Oh, oh! (*Comes to life*) That damned baron! Looks as if he's catching up with me. 257 to 256. Heh, heh. Scratch my shoe, on the second toe of my left foot. (LADISLAUS *scratches*) Heh, heh! That baron! Gambled it away I did! And that girl will have to be fixed up with a new wardrobe. Bah!

Yawns.

For every lady
Must be arrayed!

Furious.

That Baron!

He greets the Group of GENTLEMEN *who respond with gallant bows.*

Sings.

Oh, what is a baron to me!
Ha, ha, ha, a baron, indeed!
I am Count Charmant
To the ladies a true gallant!
I am the rake Charmant
A blade and an élégant!
Enfant gate of every café
With top hat and cane
Monocle and moustache
And manners none can match!

Yawns.

Countesses and princesses
Seamstresses and Negresses
And daughters of the middle-class —
Oh I'm the idol of every lass!
So suave and debonair
A man of fashion and of flair
Ah, quel chic, quel charme et quelles manières!

Enter BARON FIRULET, *thirty-five, hunting costume, shotgun, monocle, horse-whip, plumed hat. Arrogant manners. Behind him his Gamekeeper* STANLEY *carrying a gamebag.*

FIRULET: (*sings*)
Ha, ha, ha, who's this I see
Why, it's Charmant, yes, Charmant, indeed!
That tickles me!
That delights me!
Ho, ho, ho, Charmant, indeed!
I am Baron Firulet
A hunter of female prey!
With a bang, bang, bang
They're in my bag
And I'm in love again!
Oh, amour, amour!

Speaks.

Stanley, how many have I bagged so far?

STANLEY: Your Grace has 256 and Count Charmant has 257.

FIRULET:
> Phew, phew, phew, Charmant!
> Pooh, pooh, pooh, Charmant!
> I am Baron Firulet!
> And if anyone turns up his nose
> I'll put it out of joint!

GROUP OF GENTLEMEN: (*piano*)
> Oh, oh, oh, Count Charmant
> Oh, oh, oh, Baron Firulet!

CHARMANT: My dear Firulet, if my eyes do not deceive me I see that you have forsaken the intoxicating orchid gardens of our stunning cockatoo-cococo la Très Belle in order to try your hunter's luck in more . . . h'm, h'm . . . virgin territory. . . . Ha, ha, ha! Three no trumps!

Strolling arrogantly back and forth in front of the BARON.

FIRULET: My dear Charmant! Should you be harbouring any nostalgia for the intoxicating perfumes of our cockatoo-cococo la Très Belle, you're welcome to take a sniff of me — I'm positively drenched with them! Four honours in hearts!

Strolling back and forth in front of CHARMANT.

CHARMANT: Queen of spades!

FIRULET: Four clubs and a jack!

CHARMANT: I pass!

FIRULET: I pass!

CHARMANT: I double!

FIRULET: Double and redouble!

CHARMANT: I pass!

FIRULET: I pass!

GROUP OF GENTLEMEN: (*piano*)
> Oh, oh, oh, Count Charmant!
> Oh, oh, oh, Baron Firulet!

CHARMANT: Hors d'oeuvres et sauce Belmanto! But allow me,

baron, if my eyes do not deceive me you have set out with that gun to bag yourself a little doe, sapristi! But one doesn't shoot does! And I wouldn't advise poaching on someone else's territory either, sapristi. Cambridge, train de luxe, cognac, Martell, the Ritz and Carlton!

FIRULET: Tut tut, since when have moth-eaten old lechers come to the defence of innocent little does?! Wagons lits! Moulin Rouge! Are you getting snooty with me by any chance? Seven bacchantes!

CHARMANT: Four houris!

FIRULET: Two odalisques and one stenographer.

CHARMANT: One Negress, three telephone operators.

FIRULET: I double!

CHARMANT: Double and redouble!

FIRULET: A nose!

CHARMANT: A nose!

FIRULET: I pass!

CHARMANT: I pass!

GROUP OF GENTLEMEN: (*piano*)
    Oh, oh, oh, Count Charmant!
    Oh, oh, oh, Baron Firulet!

CHARMANT: (*with apathy*) Inertia.

FIRULET: (*with apathy*) Dyspepsia.

CHARMANT: Déveine.

FIRULET: Migraine.

CHARMANT: A nose.

FIRULET: A nose.

CHARMANT: I pass.

FIRULET: I pass.

FIRULET *exits with his* GAMEKEEPER.

CHARMANT: Pheasant and partridge. Provocation. Malapert. I feel faint. Ladislaus, an injection! (LADISLAUS *gives him one*) Albertine, a marvel of a lass. 257. 256. Dammit, I gambled it all away. Corso Colombo. Fricassees and delicacies. Oh, how boring. . . . (*sits down on an umbrella that serves at the same time as a chair*)

GROUP OF GENTLEMEN: (*their conversation gradually becomes more animated*)
The stools of Lord Blotton . . . the stools of Lord Blotton . . . the stools of Lord Blotton . . . the stools of Lord Blotton . . . (*with increased animation*) the stools of Lord Blotton. . . .

GENERAL: The vest of Lord Blotton.

BANKER: The vest of Lord Blotton?

MARCHIONESS: Yes, exactly, the vest of Lord Blotton!

GENERAL: In a double shade. . . .

PROFESSOR: With a turned up corner.

BANKER: What are you saying gentlemen? A vest with a turned up corner?!

Organ music. Out of the church come PRINCE *and* PRINCESS HIMALAY *in the company of* MASTER FIOR.

PRINCE: What a sermon our dear pastor delivered today in honour of our dear Lord. How nice it is that our dear Lord has been honoured by our dear pastor. Hosanna!

PRINCESS: Alleluia in excelsis! Enchantée!

They exchange greetings with the Group of GENTLEMEN.

And here is our dear guest who has just arrived straight from the avenue des Champs-Elysees, Master Fior in person. Really, my husband and I feel honoured in excelsis. . . .

PRINCE: Really, my wife and I are both overjoyed by this charming visit by our dear friend Master Fior. . . .

PRINCESS: Master Fior is the veritable dictator of style in Europe.

PRINCE: Of both men's and women's fashion. It is he who every year launches the mandatory style. . . .

PRINCESS: Gentlemen, Master Fior was gracious enough to accept my husband's invitation and has come to the Himalay castle to stage his annual sensational fashion show, featuring both men's and women's fashions. Hosanna! Alleluia in excelsis!

PRINCE: A singularly revealing event, a sign of the times: this year the voice of the dictator of European fashion will ring out from the residence of the Himalays.

GROUP OF GENTLEMEN:
Oh, oh, oh, oh, it's Master Fior!
Oh, oh, oh, oh, a fashion show!
Oh, oh, oh, oh, 'tis a marvel to behold!

FIOR: (*singing*)
For I am Fior!
Master of the mode
The fashion in vogue
Of men and women both!
Ah, ah, ah, élégance, ah, ah, ah, distinction, ah, ah, ah,
La mode, dernier cri and bon ton.

Sarcastically.

Michelangelo and Rembrandt, ha, ha, ha!
Shakespeare and Dante, ha, ha, ha!
Beethoven and Bach, ha, ha, ha!
For I'm a master of the art!
I am the one who sets the style
Who governs the taste
Messieurs, mesdames,
Who commands whiskers to bloom, stockings to blush,
    Décolletés to bulge and dress shoes to shine.
For I'm the master!
Master Fior am I!

CHARMANT: (*approaching*)
I am Charmant!
I am Charmant!

Peerless, idolized and pampered. . . .
Charmant am I
With top hat and cane
Charmant is the name
A blade and a rake
And this is the gesture I make!

FIOR & CHARMANT:
    For I am Fior (Charmant)
    The master of the mode
    Of men and women both!

FIOR: My dear count, as a matter of fact in Paris I have heard it
said that no one wears a seven-splendoured hat better than you.

CHARMANT: And just look at my vest, if you will.

GROUP:
    The stools of Lord Blotton. . . .
    The stools of Lord Blotton. . . .

PRINCE: I daresay, Master Fior, that with the help of Charmant
you will accomplish things of great proportions. Nowadays, in
these socialist-democratic and atheist-socialist times of ours,
dress has become the strongest bastion of the upper class. What
would happen if it were not for all those nuances, as it were, all
those subtleties and niceties, that mystical code which is
incomprehensible for the uninitiated and which separates the
upper class from the lower class? Manners and dress — that's
our bastion in excelsis! Hosanna! The lower class, of course,
goes to every length to adopt both our fashions and our manners and that's why it's essential to keep on introducing
innovations in order to throw them off the track. . . .

PRINCESS: It's grotesque! Never a moment's rest! A perpetual
race! No sooner do I buy a collar peignoir à la réverbère than I
see my hairdresser with the very same collar. But worst of all
are the servants. Just imagine! Yesterday I caught my maid
trying on my toilet. . . .

PRINCE: Fernanda, please. . . . Please. . . . (*Points discreetly at
the* LACKEYS *in the background*) Please . . . the servants!

PRINCESS: The servants!. . . (*Falls silent*)

BANKER: Shh. . . . My orderly used the same brand of shoe-polish as me.

PRINCE & PRINCESS: Shh. . . . The servants!

ALL: Shh. . . . The servants!

PRINCE: I hope they didn't hear anything. . . . Shh. . . .

GROUP: I hope they didn't hear. . . . Shh. . . .

PRINCE: And even if they did hear!. . . And even if they did hear!. . .

Calls.

Constantine!

His LACKEY *runs up to him.*

Brush my shoes!

GENERAL: A good idea, upon my word, with all this dust around here!
Charles!

His ORDERLY *hastens up to him.*

Polish my shoe tips, comme il faut!

PRINCE: Each must know his own place, I always say.

BANKER: It's sultry today, that's why the dust is sticking to our shoes. Maximilian! Start brushing, especially on the sides.

His LACKEY *starts brushing.*

After Paris our region must seem a trifle monotonous to you.

FIOR: Not at all!

PRINCESS: The master is just being kind to us! Reginald! Mine too!. . . (*To the* MARCHIONESS) Eulalia, your pumps are dusty too, I see. . . . Reginald, first the marchioness.

MARCHIONESS: Piti, piti.

CHARMANT: Ladislaus! First the master, then the professor and

myself! (*The* LACKEYS *polish below while the* GENTLEMEN
carry on a conversation above)

PROFESSOR: (*to* CHARMANT) I would be extremely obliged. . . .
(*as though vomiting on* FIOR)

FIOR: Pardon?!

PROFESSOR: Pardon!

PRINCESS: (*to* FIOR) Our poor inestimable professor is chroni-
cally ill with incurable vomiting. The professor's obsessive
vomiting has been treated without success by the world's most
renowned authorities. The professor, vraiment, has vomited on
the greatest specialists, on their assistants, on nurses, que sais-
je, as well as on my husband and myself. . . . In short, it would
be hard to find a piece of furniture or a person anywhere that
has not been vomited on by our dear professor. During the
summertime our dear professor vomits on flowerbeds, weeds,
herbs, worms, dogs or, for example, insects, trees, or wheelbar-
rows in vegetable gardens. . . .

PRINCE: Our dear professor's vomiting has a spasmodic, convul-
sive and doubtless chronic character. (*The* PROFESSOR *makes as
if to vomit on the* MARCHIONESS) There you are!

MARCHIONESS: Piti, piti!

PRINCE: But here comes our dear pastor.

The PRIEST *emerges from the church, approaches.*

PRIEST: The Lord be with you!

PRINCESS: What a lovely sermon our dear pastor delivered today
in honour of our dear Lord! Allow me, Reverend Father, this is
Master Fior!

PRIEST: My blessing!

FIOR: Enchanté absolument!

MARCHIONESS: Piti, piti.

PRINCE: Where was I? Oh yes, our dear Professor also vomits on
leaves, lawns, sofas, plates, fences, hedges, governesses and

hats. According to doctors it is a chronic state of nausea, queasiness, regurgitation, a state, as it were, of organic repulsion. A propos? Where is your friend, Professor, that famous horse lover and sportsman, Count Hufnagel, whom you promised to introduce to us?

PROFESSOR: (*as if vomiting*) Pardon! Count Hufnagel is still in church praying. He should be out any minute now.

PRIEST: Mrs Valentine! Dust off my sandals a little!

MRS VALENTINE, *the* PRIEST'*s housekeeper, starts brushing.*

GROUP OF GENTLEMEN: The stools of Lord Blotton . . . the stools of Lord Blotton . . . the stools of Lord Blotton. . . . (*Pianissimo*) The stools of Lord Blotton. . . .

Their voices fade away.

1st LACKEY: Hey, move over! What're you shovin' for?

2nd LACKEY: That's *my* foot!

3rd LACKEY: Now'days all da shoe tips are pointed. . . .

ORDERLY: Get away, scum, can't you see I'm polishing the General?

3rd LACKEY: Now'days all da socks got stripes on 'em.

LADISLAUS: Don't cramp me, bootblack!

PRIEST'S HOUSEKEEPER: Mercy, what a lot of trash!

2nd LACKEY: I'm outta polish. I'll lick 'em with me tongue.

3rd LACKEY: I ain't got no more wax either, but I got me a tongue.

HOUSEKEEPER: Mercy, what a lot of riff-raff!

3rd LACKEY: Hey, Max, lick here, under the heel.

LACKEYS: (*licking*)
Hey, with a li'l bit of spit
We'll lick 'em up slick!
With a lick of da tongue! Hey!
With a lick of da tongue! Hey!

GROUP OF GENTLEMEN: (*rousing themselves*) The stools of Lord
Blotton. . . .

PRINCESS: I hope that you have all received your invitations to
the ball which, I daresay, will enhance in excelsis the master's
most extraordinary fashion show in excelsis, hosanna, hosanna,
alleluia, alleluia!

PRINCE: It is our desire that this ball be worthy of the master and
the master worthy of this ball in excelsis, hosanna, hosanna!

GENTLEMEN: The stools of Lord Blotton!

PRIEST: There is nothing quite like wholesome entertainment.

GENERAL: (*to his* ORDERLY) Lick here, on the sole.

PRIEST: But here comes Count Hufnagel! A praiseworthy Chris-
tian, my dear benefactors, the last to leave God's house, glory
be to God, glory be. . . .

PRINCE: Horse lovers are always pious people. Curiously
enough, no matter now many times I've had occasion to meet a
horse lover he was always pious.

PROFESSOR:
Puke!
Puke!
Allow me, prince
Allow me, princess
Allow me, gentlemen
Count Hufnagel
My friend and companion, puke, puke, puke!

1st LACKEY: (*licking the* PRINCESS' *shoes*) What frilly undies
these high-society ladies're wearing now-days! Wait till Katie
hears about this!

2nd LACKEY: Stop peekin' under her petticoat and lick, ya son-
of-a-bitch!

PRINCESS: (*singing*) O, the count, champion without peer!

PRINCE: (*singing*) Oh, the Derby, Longchamps, Prix de Grand
Prix!

HUFNAGEL: (*singing*)
    For it's gallop, gallop, gallop!
    To gallop's my only passion. . . .
    To saunter, trot or canter —
    What sport is that I ask?
    For it's gallop, gallop, gallop!
    At a gallop I always race
    My whip will set the pace
    And off I'll gallop, one, two, three
    Hey, to gallop's my favourite sport!
    Hey, the gallop's my greatest forte!

GENTLEMEN: (*singing*)
    Hey, gallop, gallop, let's all gallop, hey,
    Gallop, at a gallop we'll gallop away!

They become motionless.

CHARMANT: (*moving slowly upstage, followed by* LADISLAUS)
Boredom. Heartburn. Déveine. Ladislaus, give me an injection.
(LADISLAUS *does so*) Why is she taking so long?

LADISLAUS: She'll be coming out any minute now!

CHARMANT: And she always sits on this bench?

LADISLAUS: Always and always.

CHARMANT: Let's have that pickpocket out here. (LADISLAUS
leads the PICKPOCKET *out from behind the bush on a leash*)
Why do you have him on a leash?

LADISLAUS: 'Cos he's got a record. Just to be on the safe side.

CHARMANT: All right. Did you get it through his head what he's
supposed to do? I'll go over it again. She'll sit down as usual
on this bench to wait for her girl friend. At a given signal the
pickpocket will sneak up from behind and whishhh . . . he'll
grab something from her, a purse or a handkerchief. . . . That's
when I catch him and introduce myself. . . . Why, of course, it's
obvious, in such a situation not only do I have the right but I'm
simply obliged to introduce myself. . . . Afterwards I'll invite
her to supper. Ha, ha, ha, I can't wait to see the expression on
Firulet's face! I'll buy her a muff.

222 _Operetta

LADISLAUS: It's in the bag, it's in the bag, Yer Grace. . . .

CHARMANT: (*somewhat embarrassed*) You see, Ladislaus, try to understand, Ladislaus, don't get me wrong, Ladislaus, don't think badly of me. . . . Naturally I'd prefer not to have to appeal to such a scoundrel for help, but I don't see, I really don't see, Ladislaus, how a person with my manners, a man of the world, a gentleman of my appearance, could simply approach some little goose sitting on a bench in front of a church. . . . Now if she were a little flirt, or a countess, or a ballet dancer, or a married woman, or an actress, then it would be a different matter. But I would never dream of approaching such a goose! On a bench! In a public square! I don't even see how I could greet her at a distance of ten feet away! Mind you, Ladislaus, ce n'est pas mon genre! But such a villain as a tramp would, it's all the same to him . . . not only could he go up to her without being introduced but he could even get hold of some of her clothing, or her purse! There you are! I can't, but he can. A curious arrangement of Nature, indeed: I can't, but he can. So you see, Ladislaus, once he's made the first move I'll have an excuse to strike up an acquaintance with her. And then I'll buy her a muff and a necklace. Do you understand, Ladislaus?

LADISLAUS:
It's in the bag! It's in the bag!
Oh, here she comes!

He hides behind the bush with the PICKPOCKET.

Organ music.

ALBERTINE *comes out of the church in the company of her parents.*

MOTHER: The pastor's sermon, what a sermon the pastor gave. Lord, what a sermon, what a sermon. . . . (*To* ALBERTINE) Stand up straight!

FATHER: It's not going to rain, but somehow the sun seems to be sort of. . . .

MOTHER: This year they're letting their curls hang down a little over the forehead . . . with one ring over the ear. . . . Have you noticed, Tini?

FATHER: The sun, h'm. . . . All the same, it's not going to raiii. . . .

MOTHER: (*to* ALBERTINE) What're you wriggling your legs like that for, why do you keep wriggling around with your legs?. . . Tini! For God's sake! People are watching!

FATHER: Hey! Look, mother! You see that character over there?

MOTHER: In the frock coat?

FATHER: Well, I'll be damned! It's Charmant!

MOTHER: Charmant? Charmant the lady-killer? Lover-boy Charmant? Look, Tini! No, don't look, what's that to you, look straight ahead! Oh, what a pain in the neck!

FATHER: In a frock coat! On his way back from a card game most likely, but hardly on his way to church, ha, ha!

MOTHER: Well, Tini? Aren't you coming?

ALBERTINE: I have to wait for Louise.

MOTHER: Oh, what a pain in the neck! Well don't be late for supper. And don't go looking around where you don't have to. Fix the hair behind your ear. Where's your needlework? Take your needlework and don't look around. . . .

FATHER: Come on, mother, let's go. Otherwise we'll be late.

The PARENTS *exeunt.*

ALBERTINE *sits down on the bench with her needlework.*

ALBERTINE: These flies. . . . Oh, there's a fly. . . . Louise. . . . A tree. . . . It's hot. . . . Hot. . . . (*She yawns*)

CHARMANT *passes by her gallantly in his top hat.* ALBERTINE *looks, yawns surreptitiously.* CHARMANT *returns, passes by her again.* ALBERTINE *looks.* CHARMANT *passes by again.* ALBERTINE *looks.* CHARMANT *passes by again.* ALBERTINE *looks.* CHARMANT *passes by again.*

God. . . . What's wrong with him?. . . I feel sleepy. . . .

She dozes off. CHARMANT *makes a sign to* LADISLAUS *who comes out from behind the bush with the* PICKPOCKET. *New*

signs from CHARMANT. LADISLAUS *unleashes the* PICKPOCKET
who, after making several pirouettes in freedom, steals up to
ALBERTINE *and gropes about her for an unduly long time.*

CHARMANT: What's he taking so long for?!

ALBERTINE: (*in her sleep*) Ooo. . . .

The PICKPOCKET *snatches a locket from her neck and runs
toward* CHARMANT *who throws him to the ground. Thunderclap. Wind, storm which immediately abate.*

CHARMANT: Tramp!

LADISLAUS: Hooligan, hooligan!

CHARMANT: (*approaching* ALBERTINE *with the locket which was
taken by the* PICKPOCKET) Forgive me, mademoiselle, for
taking the liberty to address you without having been introduced, but just now, while taking advantage of your innocent
slumber, this pickpocket had the nerve to steal this locket. I
regarded it as my duty to intervene at once. But I see that I am
addressing you without having been introduced. I am Count
Charmant.

ALBERTINE: Gee!

CHARMANT: (*singing and dancing*)
I am Count Charmant!
To the ladies a true gallant!
I am the rake Charmant!
A blade and an élégant!
Countesses and princesses
Seamstresses and Negresses
And daughters of the middle-class —
Oh, I'm the idol of every lass!
Enfant gâté of every café
With monocle and moustache
Top hat and cane. . . .
For I am Count Charmant
To the ladies a true gallant!

ALBERTINE: (*singing and dancing*)
Albertine am I!

A peach of a thing am I!
This is my hand, my foot so petite
This is my ear, my lips so sweet
This is my nose, not yours, oh no!
This is my mouth, not yours, oh no!
Oh you, my dream, my wonderful dream
Oh you, my dreams, my wonderful dreams. . . .
Oh teeth of mine, oh lips divine
Oh tongue of mine, oh ears so fine
Oh feet of mine, oh eyes so sweet
My décolleté and hands so petite
Not yours, oh no, but mine, all mine!
Oh you, my dream, oh you, my dream
Oh you, my wonderful dream!. . .

CHARMANT:
Oh you, my wonderful dream!
Now that I have had the honour of being introduced to you,
mademoiselle, may I be allowed to rest myself for a moment
beside you on this bench, at a respectable distance. . . .

ALBERTINE: Oh, please do! Your Grace is so kind! What's this?
Have I been sleeping? I was dreaming about something . . . as
if a hand. . . . (_Embarrassed_) Ooo. . . . Yes, it was a dream. As if
a hand was sort of . . . like this. . . (_She looks at_ CHARMANT
furtively, suspiciously, and touches her décolleté)

CHARMANT: (_embarrassed_) It must have been that pickpocket.

ALBERTINE: Pickpocket?

CHARMANT: Then you didn't notice anything?

ALBERTINE: What? It's hot. And all these flies. I fell asleep and
had such a dream. . . . A hand. (_She gazes suspiciously at_
CHARMANT) But what're you sitting _here_ for? What is it you
want, Your Grace? What're you sitting next to a girl like me
for?

CHARMANT: But will I be allowed to insinuate with you something on the order of a casual little flirt à la papillon? Yes,
indeed, les femmes, they're like sauce Belmanto! One

shouldn't overdo them. Hard to digest. Ladislaus, how many have I bagged?

LADISLAUS: 257, Yer Grace, and 256 for Baron Firulet.

CHARMANT: There you are! Heartburn. Boredom.

ALBERTINE: Oh, oh!

CHARMANT: Nachgeschmack!

ALBERTINE: Oh!

CHARMANT: Over-indulgence. Catarrh. Statistics and migraines. The law of great numbers.

ALBERTINE: Oh!

CHARMANT: But now that we're sitting her on this bench in the shade, I see no other alternative but to invite you to Maxim's. If I still tolerate women then it's only those who are stuffed, and only those stuffed with food from a good restaurant. A woman with a good poulard in her belly is still more appetizing than the same woman who is crammed, so to speak, with potatoes or buckwheat. I invite you to Maxim's. Shall we say: oysters stuffed with lobster, ostrich eggs à la cocotte, fleur de saumon, hollandaise, pheasant. . . .

ALBERTINE: Oh!

CHARMANT: Ladislaus, a pill! But let us hope, by a subdued light under a scarlet shade, with the intoxicating sounds of a gypsy band in the background, ah, ah, hors d'oeuvres and bacchantes, with champagne foaming in our blood, gypsy trills, your fragrance inflames the senses, I lean forward, you retreat, I lean forward, you retreat, evoe, evoe, you retreat, ha, and then Iiii. . . . ah, gypsies, oysters, I begin to. . . .

ALBERTINE: Oh, dear! To undress me?

CHARMANT: Oh, no! Not undress you! Dress you! A muff made of moles' tails from Worth's.

ALBERTINE: Oh!

CHARMANT: Stockings made of Parisian mist!

ALBERTINE: Oh!

CHARMANT: Pink unmentionables with a meringue trim!

ALBERTINE: Oh!

CHARMANT: Jupe bombée, crème apricot!

ALBERTINE: Oh!

CHARMANT: A blouse with mushrooms in a sauce provençale. . . .

ALBERTINE: Oh!

CHARMANT: A bonnet with panache de légumes!

Darkness, wind, storm, thunder.

ALBERTINE:
Count! Instead of undressing me
You want to dress me!

CHARMANT: Pardon? Pardon? Pardon?

ALBERTINE:
Can't you see.
Under my dress
I'm naked as can be!

Thunderclap.

GROUP OF GENTLEMEN: (*awaking, piano, crescendo, dramatically*) The stools of Lord Blotton, the stools of Lord Blotton, the stools of Lord Blotton. . . . (*They become motionless*)

CHARMANT: (*bewildered*) A negligée with lace, trimmed with early-autumn fox, silver fox, or a déshabillé of raw silk with Scottish flounce. . . .

ALBERTINE: Nude. . . . I want to be nude!

Thunderclap.

GROUP OF GENTLEMEN: (*piano, desperately*) The stools of Lord Blotton, the stools of Lord Blotton, the stools of Lord Blotton. . . .

They become motionless.

LACKEYS: (*wildly*) Hoooooooo! (*wind*)

ALBERTINE *flees.*

CHARMANT: (*bewildered*) This is the first time I've ever known a
woman who'd rather be undressed than dressed. . . .

GROUP OF GENTLEMEN: (*fortissimo, wildly*) The stools of Lord
Blotton!

Enter FIRULET *with his* GAMEKEEPER.

FIRULET: (*assailing* CHARMANT *with laughter*)

Ha, ha, ha, ha-ha, ha, ha, ha!

Ha, ha, ha, ha-ha, ha, ha, ha!

CHARMANT: (*defending himself*)

Ha, ha, ha, ha-ha, ha, ha, ha!

Ha, ha, ha, ha-ha, ha, ha, ha!

FIRULET: Got away, eh? My condolences! That's a blow, ha, ha!
Three no trumps!

CHARMANT: (*with consternation*) I don't understand. . . . I don't
understand. . . . I don't understand. . . . (*Perfunctorily, against*
FIRULET) Ha, ha, ha!

FIRULET: What don't you understand, Count? (*Against*
CHARMANT) Ha, ha, ha!

CHARMANT: (*against* FIRULET) Ha, ha, ha!. . . No, I don't understand! You see, Baron, while I was flirting I hinted that I was
going to buy her this and that by way of a wardrobe. But what
does she want? To be nude!

FIRULET: Nude?

CHARMANT: Nude, tout court!

FIRULET: Excuse me, do you mean, Count, that instead of a
negligée, chemise, déshabillé, dessous . . . just those loins,
thighs, haunches, collarbones?. . . Nothing else?

CHARMANT:
Nothing!

The body.
The body and nothing else. . . .

Wind.

FIRULET: Oh, what a roar nature is making!

CHARMANT: Oh, what a roar nature is making!

BOTH: Oh, a roar, a roar, a roar!

CHARMANT: (*pensively*) The body.

FIRULET: (*pensively*) The body.

CHARMANT: In the nude.

FIRULET: In the nude.

CHARMANT: And nothing else.

FIRULET: And nothing else.

BOTH: And a roar, and a roar, and a roar!

> LADISLAUS *emerges from behind the bush with the* PICKPOCKET *on a leash.*

LADISLAUS: Yer Grace?

CHARMANT: Well?

LADISLAUS: What about this mongrel? Let him go, turn him over to the police, or what?

FIRULET: A dog or a street urchin? Where did you pick him up?

CHARMANT: Stop, baron! Wait, baron! I'm beginning to understand. . . . Ahh. . . ahh . . . ahh. . . . You see, she was sleeping on the bench. I turned that pickpocket loose on her so he could steal something, then I was supposed to pounce on him and introduce myself. . . . That was the plan! But. . . . Well, now I understand!

FIRULET: Well? Go on!

CHARMANT: (*to himself, alarmed*) In her sleep she felt his hand under her bosom . . . but she thought it was *my* hand . . . that it was *me*!

FIRULET: I beg your pardon?! You, count, stick your hand under her bosom, here, on this bench, underneath a tree, in a public square, and without even being introduced to her?! What a preposterous idea!

GROUP OF GENTLEMEN: (*dramatically*) The stools of Lord Blotton!

CHARMANT: She thought it was *me*! That I was the one who reached down there! That's why she felt like being nude. Nude with me! Good heavens!

Wind, but without force.

FIRULET: I beg your pardon. I beg your pardon?!. . . Nude? Nude with you, count? You mean, you mean, without your cane, without your monocle, without your top hat, without your pants and without your drawers?

CHARMANT: She wants to be nude with me.

FIRULET: (*holding his sides*)
Ha, ha, ha, ha-ha, ha, ha, ha!
Ha, ha, ha, ha-ha, ha, ha, ha!

LADISLAUS:
Ho, ho, ho! Ho, ho, ho!

GROUP OF GENTLEMEN:
Ha, ha, ha, ha, ha, ha!

GROUP OF LACKEYS:
Ha, ha, ha, ha, ha, ha!

CHARMANT: (*singing*)
What is it now, my dear baron?
What do you mean? Why that laugh?
I won't tolerate it! Now off with you! Off!
An impertinence! What are you implying?

FIRULET: (*singing*)
Charmant in the nude, Charmant in the nude!
Ha, ha, ha, horray, horrah!
Ha, ha, ha, Charmant in the raw!
Charmant in the nude, Charmant in the nude!

They parade before one another arrogantly.

CHARMANT: Four honours in hearts!

FIRULET: A grand slam in diamonds!

CHARMANT: A double in suit!

FIRULET: I double and redouble!

CHARMANT: Three no trumps!

FIRULET: A grand slam in spades.

CHARMANT: I pass!

FIRULET: I pass! My dear Count Charmant, when you're getting undressed don't forget to call me so I can come and admire, ha, ha, ha, ha, ha, ha!

Exits with his GAMEKEEPER.

CHARMANT: (*crushed*)
Impudent fellow!
Malapert!

Sits down on the umbrella-stool.

I gambled and lost. . . .

GROUP OF GENTLEMEN: (*pianissimo, crescendo*) The stools of Lord Blotton, the stools of Lord Blotton, the stools of Lord Blotton, the stools of Lord Blotton. . . .

PROFESSOR: Puke. . . .

BANKER: Heartburn. Acid indigestion. Over-indulgence. . . .

PRINCE: Yes, yes, gentlemen, that's the gospel truth. . . . I too am suffering in excelsis, and so is my wife, from something like over-abundance, repletion, over-eating, as though . . . yes, as though it were a case, so to say, of too many petits fours, creams, dress-coats, pastries, milliners, coiffures, compotes, collars, desserts, meringues, whip-creams, que sais-je, lackeys, buttons, carriages. . . .

PROFESSOR: Puke. . . .

PRINCE: That's it exactly! You took it right out of my mouth, Professor!

PRINCESS: There is some sort of indigestion in the air.

GENERAL: Plenitude.

BANKER: Over-indulgence.

MARCHIONESS: Piti, piti.

CHARMANT *exits with* LADISLAUS *and the* PICKPOCKET *on a leash.*

PRIEST: Oh Lord, what an age we're living in! Heaven protect us!

PRINCESS: Master, all our hope lies in you. The master, if you please, will renovate our fashions! The master will bring men's and women's fashions up to date!

FIOR: (*musing*)
Renovate
Men's and women's fashions?...

GROUP OF GENTLEMEN:
Oh yes, oh yes, oh yes!

FIOR:
It's very well to say!
It's very well to say: create a new fashion!
Invent a new style! But what sort of new style?
The style.... The style cannot march contrary to the times
The style *is* time. The style is history!
Am I mistaken when I say
That the style is history?

PRINCE:
It's history!

BANKER:
The style is history!

GENERAL:
Yes, it's history!

HUFNAGEL:
History!

PRINCESS: (*to the* PRINCE)
    Is the style really history?

PRINCE:
    Yes, the style is history!

GROUP OF GENTLEMEN: (*lifting up their arms*)
    The . . . style . . . is . . . history!

Silence.

FIOR:
    History. . . .
    I am Fior! A master am I! Master Fior!
    To furnish modern man with a brand-new look?
    Oh, for the masters of old it was easy to invent!
    But how difficult it is today. . . .

    What will come in five, ten, fifteen years? What will the future
    bring? How time does race. . . .

    Oh, how troubled I am by an age I can't divine!
    In the womb of the present is the future contained. . . .
    O inscrutable form!

    Russia . . . England . . . Maritime policy . . . Delcasse . . . the
    Balkans . . . Socialism . . . the Kronprinz. . . . Where to? How? In
    which direction? Towards which goal? What sort of pant leg
    should I propose when I don't even know whether ten years from
    now pant legs will be worn? Perhaps the clothing of the future
    will be made of feathers or mental rings. . . . The future. . . .

    The future is a dark chasm, an enigma
    History is without a face!

GROUP OF GENTLEMEN: History is without a face!

PRINCESS: Ladies and Gentlemen, let us respect, in excelsis, the
    creative anguish of our unfathomable creator, the master. . . .

FIOR: How time does race! Take that bench, for example. It looks
    like it's standing still, but oh how it's racing! It's racing and
    racing. . . . Where though? Where to? In which direction?
    Toward which goal? Oh God, everything is racing, racing!

HUFNAGEL: (*singing*)
Oh, for it's gallop, gallop, gallop
To gallop's my only passion!
To saunter, trot or canter
What sport is that I ask!
For it's gallop, gallop, gallop!
At a gallop I always race
My whip will set the pace
And off I'll gallop, one, two, three
Hey, to gallop's my favourite sport
Hey, the gallop's my greatest forte!

GROUP OF GENTLEMEN: (*astonished*) The stools of Lord
Blotton. . . .

PRINCE: (*somewhat startled*) I beg your pardon! Gallop? Why, of
course! If the shoe fits wear it, as the saying goes.

PRINCESS: Our dear count is injecting a note of truly sporting
optimism into our pessimistic conversation! Merci! Merci!

HUFNAGEL: I'm not used to being unsaddled. No, I'm not used to
being unsaddled. The gallop is my speciality. Forgive me,
Master, but I do not share your anxiety. That bench? Race?
Gallop? To an unknown destination? Well, so what if it is? I'll
mount it, I'll race, I'll gallop! History? Race? Gallop? Well, so
what if it is? I'll mount it, I'll face, I'll gallop! I'm not used to
being unsaddled!

PROFESSOR: Puuuu. . . .

PRINCESS: (*to the* PROFESSOR) Please don't interrupt!

HUFNAGEL: The whole trick is to squeeze tightly with your knees
and thighs, let go of the reins a little and then whip! Why, I
may even have an idea for the Master in regard to this fashion
show. . . .

PRINCE: Oh, if you have an idea, count, then by all means tell us,
because we haven't had any ideas for ages. . . . Oh, what am I
saying?. . .

FIOR: (*to himself*)
An idea

What sort of an idea?
Night, darkness!

HUFNAGEL: Now if your nag starts to bolt the best thing to do is
to let up on the reins, give him his head, only don't let yourself
be unsaddled. . . . Now here's what I would suggest:

Let the ball that's to be staged
Be a masquerade ball!
Let the ball be masked
Exactly like our age!

GROUP OF GENTLEMEN: And what then? What then? What then?

HUFNAGEL:
A masquerade ball, a costume ball
In the castle's most splendid hall
Filled with costumes more bizarre
Than any age has seen thus far!

GROUP OF GENTLEMEN: And what then? What then? What then?

HUFNAGEL:
Amid this surge of costumes droll
Some of the guests will in sacks be robed
A sack of cloth worn upside down
With a hole at the top for the head to show
But the head of each shall also be masked
So that none of the guests the others will know!

GROUP OF GENTLEMEN: And what then? What then? What then?

HUFNAGEL: At a given signal from the Master the sacks will fall,
and the style of the future will be revealed. . . . Is everything
clear? Now why should the Master have to invent the new style
by himself? Wouldn't it be better to sound out public opinion
first, so to speak? To find out which way the wind is blowing?
To discover the latest fads, the latest crazes, the latest whims?
We shall invite everyone to take part in a contest for the new
fashion. Each of the guests will design a costume of his choice
and over this costume each will put on a sack. After the sacks
have fallen and the costumes have been revealed, the Master
will award the prizes and drawing inspiration from these

costumes he will improvise the definitive style of men's and
women's fashion for the years to come. Any objections? Well,
come on, then! Into the saddle and off at a gallop!

Hey, gallop, gallop!
I'm off at a gallop!
Give him the whip!
One, two, three!

PRINCE: Hey, not so fast! Slow down!. . .

HUFNAGEL:
Bucephalus!
Rear up now and gallop away!
So long as I stay in the saddle, hey-hey!

GROUP OF GENTLEMEN:
Rear up now and gallop away!
So long as I stay in the saddle, hey-hey!

PROFESSOR: (*unexpectedly*) Puke!

PRINCESS: I beg your pardon?

PROFESSOR: Puke!

PRINCE: Come again?

PROFESSOR: Puke!

BANKER: What did you say?

PROFESSOR: Puke!

FIOR: (*musing*)
Sacks . . . h'm. . . .
Not a bad idea, perhaps. . . .
Yes . . . yes. . . .

HUFNAGEL: So off at a gallop!

PRINCE: At full gallop!

PRINCESS: At full tilt!

BANKER: Forward, at full speed!

GENERAL: Give him the whip!

HUFNAGEL: And gallop, gallop!

PRIEST: In full career!

GROUP OF GENTLEMEN: (*shouting*) The stools of Lord Blotton!

PRINCESS: To the castle everybody!

PROFESSOR: (*aside*) Puke, puke, puke!

> *The* LADIES *and* GENTLEMEN *exeunt, leaving behind the* LACK-
> EYS *in a kneeling position.* FIOR *hesitates; he does not go out
> with the others but continues contemplating the bench.*

FIOR:
>   To gallop . . . yes, yes. . . . To gallop. . . .
>   How easy it is to mount a horse
>   But more terrifying still than the gallop of any steed
>   Is the gallop born of immobility
>   A motionless gallop in full career!

> *He touches the bench.*

>   Where are you heading, bench?
>   Where are you charging like a madman?
>   Where to?
>   Toward which goal?
>   Oh, everything, everything, these trees and stones,
>   Houses and church, earth and sky
>   Is a galloping horse! But I shall not move!
>   I'll become a statue in order to impede
>   That galloping rush, that mad stampede!

> *He stands motionless.*

>   Perhaps this galloping will stop. . . .

> *Solemnly, lifting up his arms.*

>   It's no use! It's no use!
>   I'm racing too! Flying! Galloping!
>   A galloping horse!

> *Thunderclap.* FIOR *exits.*

LACKEYS: (*furiously*)
>   Slaughter 'em!
>   Strangle 'em!

Butcher 'em!
Murder 'em!
Mutilate 'em!
Massacre 'em!
And gallop, gallop, hoppety hop!
And gallop, gallop, hoppety hop!

Curtain.

ACT TWO

*Entrance to the Himalay Castle; to the left, the entrance to the
ballroom; upstage, a platform for the fashion show.* PRINCE *and*
PRINCESS *welcome the guests.* LACKEYS.

GUESTS: (*entering*)
Oh, oh, oh, oh, it's the ball after all!
Oh, oh, oh, oh, 'tis indeed a ball!

PRINCE & PRINCESS:
Oh, oh, oh, oh, welcome, welcome!
Oh, oh, oh, oh, greetings, greetings!

Enter CHARMANT *in a hunting costume leading* ALBERTINE *in a
mantle and, on a leash, his* PICKPOCKET, *who hops and sniffs
about on all fours;* CHARMANT *is loaded down with several
boxes of ladies' garments.*

PRINCE: (*to the* LACKEYS)
Hey over there, the windows!
Hey, it's autumn, it's autumn!

PRINCESS: What a terrible draught!

PRINCE: My word, it's Charmant.

CHARMANT: It's not hard to guess. How are you, mamma? And
you, father? Many guests?

PRINCESS: Quite a lot, in excelsis. I hear that you took quite a
beating at cards again. But tell me, what kind of creature is that
you're holding on leash? Not a dog, I hope. I simply won't
tolerate any dogs at my balls.

CHARMANT: But anyone can see it's a rather harmless dog. It's a
kind of lackey in a wild and primitive state, and I'm holding

him on a leash because it's safer. He might steal something. . . .
Allow me, this is Mademoiselle Alberta Kruzek, daughter of
the shopkeper from the marketplace. . . .

PRINCE: Mes hommages! (*Aside*) But I don't quite understand in
what capacity you're bringing this shopkeeper's daughter here.
Unless, as I suspect, in the capacity of a flirt. . . .

PRINCESS: I protest!

CHARMANT: Right away a scene. Of course, I won't deny, sauce
sapristi, I did buy her that little hat and Firulet, who always
feels obliged to imitate me, did buy her those pumps and, as a
matter of fact, we did pay for this and that of her wardrobe. But
she still refuses to accept any jewellery, let alone cheques so
she is not a coquette. The truth of the matter is, papa, she's a
model. I suggested her to Fior for the fashion show. Fior needs
models for presenting his creations, and since she does have a
good figure. . . . The castle will soon have a chance to see for
itself . . . and to get acquainted with her. . . . Heartburn. Dol-
drums. Ladislaus, an injection! (LADISLAUS *gives him an
injection*)

PRINCESS: Pardon, tsk, tsk, if this coquette is a model, then being
a model she might be a coquette too, tsk, tsk, pardon, pardon,
in excelsis, tsk, tsk!

PRINCE: Tsk, tsk, tsk! (*Aside to* ALBERTINE) You're cute!

PRINCESS: Quiet!

Enter the BANKER *and the* GENERAL *in sacks from which only
their heads are exposed. On their faces, masks.*

Now there are some jolly little masks for you!

PRINCE:
Hidden in those sacks
Is the secret of the future!

PRINCE & PRINCESS:
Ah, ah, ah, ah, it's the ball after all!
Ah, ah, ah, ah, welcome all, welcome all!

BANKER: (*hopping*) Gneeam Hautoo Koopotoo loo!

GENERAL: (*hopping*) Mneeootoobabooneemmooo. . . .

BANKER: Boooo! Plap!

PRINCESS: Goodness gracious!

PRINCE: My queen, that's only to enhance their disguises! Ha, ha!

PRINCESS: Ahh. . . .

GENERAL: Ploop.

BANKER: Plap.

PRINCE & PRINCESS: (*politely*) Ploop plap ploop plap ploop plap!

PRINCESS: (*aghast*) Ahh. . . .

PRINCE & PRINCESS:
Ah, ah, ah, ah, it's the ball after all!
Ah, ah, ah, ah, 'tis indeed a ball!

CHARMANT: (*To* ALBERTINE) Only please don't be nervous, feel completely at ease. . . . This way, please. (*He shows her to the platform*) Master Fior will be along any minute now. Sauce bourguignonne. (*To the* PICKPOCKET) Shh. . . .

LADISLAUS: He's a ferocious one, Yer Grace.

ALBERTINE *takes off her mantle with the help of* CHARMANT. *A magnificent toilet, lavish coiffure, boa, gloves, necklace, parasol, a hat in her hand, muff, etc. . . . Weighed down with all this she can hardly move.*

ALL: Ooooo!

CHARMANT: (*a little embarrassed*) Well, you see, mamma, the necklace is from me, the boa from Firulet, the gloves from me, the parasol from Firulet. . . . (*To the* PICKPOCKET) Shh. . . .

LADISLAUS: He's a ferocious man, Yer Grace.

PRINCE & PRINCESS: (*to the new arrivals upstage*) Greetings, ah, greetings!

Enter the MARCHIONESS *in a sack, masked.*

242 _____Operetta

PRINCESS: Eh?

MARCHIONESS: (*hopping around awkwardly*)
Glooglooglooglooglooo.

PRINCE: Eh?

MARCHIONESS: Glooglooglooglooglooglooglooglooglooo!

PRINCESS: Eh?

PRINCE: Uh?

MARCHIONESS: Glooglooglooglooglooglooglooglooo!

PRINCESS: (*to the* PRINCE) But, Maurice, please, this is impossible. . . . Try to communicate with them somehow. Say
something to them.

PRINCE: Me? Say something? (*Cautiously*) Gooa, gooa?

MARCHIONESS: Gloogloogloot!

BANKER: Ploot plat!

PRINCE: Plote pleet (*To the* PRINCESS) They're talking freely
enough, only no one knows what's being said.

The MARCHIONESS *makes a terrific leap to one side.*

PRINCESS: What was that which jumped?

GENERAL & BANKER: (*in a frenzy*) Plaplaplaplaplaooooooooo!

PRINCE & PRINCESS:
Ah, ah, ah, ah, it's the ball after all!
Ah, ah, ah, ah, 'tis indeed a ball!

The stools of Lord Blotton (*Greeting the newly arrived guests
upstage*) Welcome, welcome!

Enter FIRULET *dressed in hunting costume like* CHARMANT,
leading on a leash a PICKPOCKET *identical to that of*
CHARMANT.

CHARMANT: (*seeing this*) Ugh! What a nerve!

FIRULET: Three no trumps!

CHARMANT: Four honours in hearts!

FIRULET: A little slam in triumphs!

CHARMANT: I double!

FIRULET: Double and redouble!

CHARMANT: I pass!

FIRULET: I pass!

They parade before one another vehemently with their PICK-POCKETS. *Throughout this act the* PICKPOCKETS *behave like dogs which, greatly excited by the ball, sniff about, pull at their leashes and bare their teeth.*

CHARMANT: (*coming to a halt*) Really, sapristi, this is too much. I buy her a hat, you buy her a boa, I buy her gloves, you buy her pumps, I come in a hunting costume with a wild pickpocket on a leash, you come in a hunting costume with a wild pickpocket on a leash! Well now, if that isn't plagiarism!

FIRULET: I double! I double and redouble! And what did you think, count? That you had a monopoly on pickpockets? I have just as much right as you. You have yours (*More softly, as though ashamed*) and I have mine. . . .

CHARMANT: (*lowering his voice*) What a nerve, I say. . . .

ALBERTINE: (*unexpectedly*) Mmmmm . . . mm. . . .

PRINCESS: And that? What's that?

ALBERTINE: Mm. . . (*She falls asleep while standing up*)

PRINCE: Looks as if she's gone to sleep. . . .

An autumn wind howls, the windows rattle, the light flickers.

What weather, honestly!

CHARMANT: (*lowering his voice*) Once in a while she just falls asleep. . . .

ALBERTINE: (*in her sleep*)
It's hard. . . .
Oh, how hard it is. . . .

FIRULET: (*lowering his voice, to* CHARMANT) Does she fall asleep often?

CHARMANT: (*in anguish, to* FIRULET) Ever since that pickpocket stuck his hand under her bosom she's continually falling asleep. She dozes off every chance she gets.

ALBERTINE: (*in her sleep*) It's hard. . . .

FIRULET: She keeps falling asleep because she would like him to stick his hand down there again . . . under her bosom, or some-where else. . . . (*To his* PICKPOCKET) Shh. . . .

CHARMANT: (*To his* PICKPOCKET) Shh. . . Down Boy!

To FIRULET.

She wants him to stick his hand down there? You mean she would like *me* to stick my hand down there! Me! (*Ashamed*) She keeps thinking that it was *my* hand. . . .

FIRULET: (*vehemently*) Stick your hand down there, count!

CHARMANT: What do you take me for anyway?

FIRULET: Stick your hand down there, count!

CHARMANT: What do you take me for anyway?!

Quiet.

ALBERTINE: (*in her sleep*) Nude. . . .

FIRULET: What did she say?

CHARMANT: Nude. . . .

FIRULET: Nude?

CHARMANT: Nude. . . .

FIRULET: Nude? Nude? She would like to be nude?

CHARMANT: Nude . . . with me. . . .

FIRULET:
Undress yourself, count!

If it's nudity she wants
Undress yourself!

CHARMANT: Have you gone mad, baron?

FIRULET: If she wants to be in the nude with you, then undress
yourself, count!

CHARMANT: Undress myself?

FIRULET: Ha, ha, ha!

CHARMANT: (*furious*) What is it now, baron? What's wrong?

FIRULET: Ha, ha, ha, the count in the nude!

CHARMANT: What's got into you?

FIRULET: The count in the buff, ha, ha, ha!

CHARMANT: The baron in the buff, ha, ha, ha!

FIRULET: The count without his drawers, ha, ha, ha!

CHARMANT: The baron without his drawers, ha, ha, ha!

FIRULET: I double!

CHARMANT: Double and redouble!

FIRULET: I pass!

CHARMANT: I pass!

Silence.

ALBERTINE: (*in her sleep*) Nuuuude. . . .

CHARMANT & FIRULET: There she is again!

FIRULET: Oh, how annoying!

CHARMANT: (*feverishly*) . . . she thinks that I was the one who
stuck my hand down there, that I was the one who stuck my
hand down there. . . .

FIRULET:
It was not the count, but that tramp
That rogue, that thief, that scamp,

That hooligan whose hand she felt!
It's he who should be in the nude with her
For he in the nude is more pleasing than you!

CHARMANT:
I beg your pardon, baron?! What do you mean?!
Would you compare me with him? With that street urchin?

FIRULET: That's right, I'm comparing you, ha, ha, ha!

CHARMANT:
Then better compare
Those limbs of yours, all rancid with age
With the nudity of that dog, more pleasing by far!

FIRULET:
Watch out, my dear count,
Or I'll stick on you my hound!
And that might prove disastrous!

CHARMANT: Mine is more ferocious! Stick him!

FIRULET: Stick him, boy! Stick him!

The PICKPOCKETS *spring at each other, growling.*

MARCHIONESS, GENERAL, BANKER: Toolatoohoolagiioooogiiooo!

FIRULET: (*menacingly*) I'll mug your mug you mug!

CHARMANT: (*menacingly*) I'll mug your mug you mug!

They exeunt with their PICKPOCKETS. *It grows dark . . . and
there arises a sort of cheerless, forlorn dawn. Upstage, two
gentlemen appear in top hats, rigid, in black: the seconds.*
CHARMANT *and* FIRULET *enter from either side of the stage in
long black cloaks, top hats, with pistols, each holding with his
left hand his* PICKPOCKET *on a leash. Bows.*

SECONDS: Fire!

CHARMANT *and* FIRULET *shoot. They miss each other, change
places, bowing to one another in passing.*

SECONDS: Fire!

They shoot. They miss each other. General depression.

CHARMANT: I pass!

FIRULET: I pass!

Great dismay. Dejection. They exeunt together with their SECONDS.

PRINCE & PRINCESS: (*recovering*)
The stools of Lord Blotton.
The stools of Lord Blotton.

ALL:
Oh, oh, oh, oh, it's the ball after all!
Oh, oh, oh, oh, 'tis indeed a ball!

MARCHIONESS, BANKER, GENERAL: Geeaoogeeaootooeeooee-
ooooooooooaaaa!

PRINCESS:
Oh please, Maurice, I beg you so
As silly as it seems, I'm dying to know
Who could be hidden inside those sacks. . . .
Oh Maurice, I'd simply love to take a peek!

PRINCE:
You'd better not peek inside those sacks
I advise you, my dear, to be discreet!

Enter the PRIEST *in a cassock.*

PRINCESS: (*alarmed*) Oh dear, what kind of black creature is that, Maurice?

PRINCE: Why, it's our dearly beloved pastor of our dearly be-loved Lord!

PRIEST: God be with you!

PRINCE & PRINCESS: God be with you! God be with you!

MARCHIONESS: Geeaooo!

PRINCESS: Oh dear! Someone just bit me . . . something just bit me. . . .

PRINCE: Keep calm, Fernanda!

ALL:
 Ah, ah, ah, it's the ball after all!
 Ah, ah, ah, 'tis indeed a ball!

PRIEST: Et fiat voluntas tua!

Enter the PROFESSOR *and* HUFNAGEL *in sacks and masks.*

PROFESSOR: Ooooooooooooo!

HUFNAGEL: Rrrrrrrrrrrr!

PRINCE: Welcome, ooooooooo, welcome, rrrrrrrrrr, hosanna in
 excelsis, ooooooooo rrrrrrrrrrrrr welcome!

 Keep calm, Fernanda!

MARCHIONESS: (*suddenly*) Geeaoo!

*Quiet. The windows rattle; a wind can be heard blowing
somewhere in the distance.*

PRINCESS: (*stupefied*) Somehow it's boring. . . .

Quiet.

ALBERTINE: (*in her sleep*) Nude. . . . Nude. . . .

PRINCESS: Oh, it's her again, what's wrong with her, what's got
 into her, what does she want, Maurice, what's the matter with
 her, what's got into her? All we need now is for everyone to fall
 asleep!

Enter FIOR *in a frock coat with an orchid in his buttonhole.*

ALL: O, O, O, O Fior, O Fior, O Fior!

FIOR: I am Fior. . . .

ALL: (*with sudden animation*)
 Oh, oh, oh, a ball after all, a ball!
 Oh, oh, oh, 'tis indeed a ball!

FIOR:
 Oh, oh, oh, a ball after all!
 Oh, oh, oh, this is the ball!

ALL: O Fior, O Fior, O Fior, O Fior!

FIOR:

> A flood of lights, a masked swarm
> A wondrous night of hidden forms
> A forest of costumes not yet born!
> Here is the marble where dormant lies
> That which the master will summon to life!

ALL: O master, O master, O master, O master!

FIOR:

> A dark deluge of bizarre ideas
> Let each his own in secret dream
> Then will the master from out of these schemes
> The statue of the future to the world reveal!

ALL: O master, O master, O master, O master!

FIOR: Ah, I see, my model is already standing on the platform! Excellent! Only she looks, parole d'honneur, as if she's just come home from at least ten boutiques. . . . I shall take my place here together with the Prince and Princess as the jury. After the sacks have been removed, the sackbearers will march by . . . yes . . . please place a stool over here. . . . Good. But somehow there's something. . . . What's going on here? Eh?

ALBERTINE: (*in her sleep*) Nude. . . .

FIOR: Eh?

ALBERTINE: Nuu. . . .

PRINCE: She's drowsing. . . . Yesterday she had supper with Charmant, sauce Languedoc, crème soubise, and now she's dreaming about something. . . .

PRINCESS: She's always dreaming, but you'd think she could dream about something else now and then. . . . Nudity indeed! What nudity, anyway?! Nudity, ladies and gentlemen, is demagogic, it's downright socialist. (*In a thunderous voice*) For what would happen if the common people discovered that our arse is identical to their own?

FIOR: Eh?

PRINCE: (*in a thunderous voice*) As a matter of fact, in a way

Fernanda is right. What would happen if they found out that
our arse was not very different from theirs?. . .

PRINCESS: (*in a thunderous voice*) It's precisely the arse, I wish
to emphasize, the arse! Because when it comes to the hands or
the feet or the extremities in general, or even the face, our
breed is quite apparent. But the arse! (*To her* LACKEY)
Jonathan, brush my shoes!

PRINCE: (*in a thunderous voice*) To be sure, even in our circles
there are faces which are inferior to arses. (*To his* LACKEY)
Polish mine, too. They're dusty.

PRINCESS: (*in a thunderous voice*) That's true too, one simply
has to agree with Maurice. Please, the master's shoe tips are
dusty too. (*To her* LACKEY) Brush them off!

The LACKEYS *start brushing the shoes of the* LADIES *and*
GENTLEMEN.

PRINCE: Just imagine, master! I have a cousin who picks his
nose. Now curiously enough, the moment anyone finds out that
he's the Prince de Concombre de la Cuille de Godalaise, then,
of course, his nose-picking becomes a princely nose-picking
and everything's as it should be.

PRINCESS: But if somebody doesn't know that he's the Prince de
Concombre de la Cuille de la Godelaise then his nose-picking
becomes something positively vulgar.

PRINCE: Exactly. Which leads me to suspect that the aristocracy
does not possess a single peculiarity which might distinguish it
from the common people, except for one, but one which is
decisive — namely, that it is the aristocracy. And what, ladies
and gentlemen, is the aristocracy? It's the aristocracy, pure and
simple. The aristocracy is the aristocracy. Please note, for
example, that I am in no way superior to my lackeys and, que
sais-je, I may even be inferior. It's no secret, after all, that I'm
an intellectual dunce, an ignoramus, a loafer, a dullard, a bore,
an imbecile, a glutton, a gourmand and a nincompoop. And my
wife, tout le monde le sait, is a consummate ass. But since I am
Prince Himalay, my imbecility is, as it were, whose imbecility?

Prince Himalay's. While the imbecility of some Mr Schmidt, for example, is just the imbecility of Mr Schmidt tout court. . . . There's the whole difference!

PRINCESS: What Maurice says is the gospel truth, the gospel truth! But now I invite everyone into the ballroom! If you please!

PRINCE: We invite you in excelsis!

Exeunt the PRINCE *and* PRINCESS, FIOR *and the* SACKBEARERS *except the* PROFESSOR *and* HUFNAGEL. HUFNAGEL *sticks out his foot to the* LACKEYS.

PROFESSOR: P-p-puke. . . .

HUFNAGEL: A kick of the foot.

PROFESSOR: P-p-puuu. . . .

HUFNAGEL: A kick of the foot. . . .

Silence.

PROFESSOR: Let's go into the ballroom. P-p-puuuu. . . .

HUFNAGEL: Just a moment. First our shoes. Let me have your foot. (*To the* LACKEYS) Clean it!

LACKEYS: Polish it!

PROFESSOR: Why all this polishing? (*Mysteriously*) What do you have in mind, 'count'? What are your real plans, 'count'? Joseph! It's Joseph I'm collaborating with, it's Joseph I brought into the castle, it's Joseph I introduced as the famous horse lover, Count Hufnagel. . . . But let's be more careful! For God's sake, let's be careful, that is, without God!

HUFNAGEL: A kick of the foot.

PROFESSOR: A kick of the foot, a kick of the foot, but I have to be kept informed, otherwise I'll puu. . . . I'll puuuu. . . . I'll puuuuuuuke out Joseph, myself, this castle, the whole neighbourhood, the globe, the Milky Way and the whole immensity of the celestial vault in my cosmic, metaphysical-physical and phenomenological vomit.

HUFNAGEL: A kick of the foot. (*He gives him a kick in the rear*)

PROFESSOR: Oh, I feel better now! Thanks! (*Confidentially*) But watch out they don't recognize you, Joseph!

HUFNAGEL: (*to the* LACKEYS) Shine them!

LACKEYS: Polish them!

HUFNAGEL: Polish them!

LACKEYS: Shine them!

HUFNAGEL: (*listening intently to the music coming from the adjoining room*) Oh, how dreamy that waltz makes you feel, ho, ho!

PROFESSOR: Enough of this! Let's go!

1st LACKEY: Hey, stop pushing! Mind yer own business!

2nd LACKEY: Stop gassing! What's the use of gassing? Shit!

3rd LACKEY: Whose foot is that?

1st LACKEY: It belongs to that new bloke, that count who's always racing around on a horse.

2nd LACKEY: That's a pretty big foot, huh . . . you'd've never thought it was a count's foot . . . it's a big one alright . . . just like ours, huh?

3rd LACKEY: A big foot. You're right. Just like ours. Have a look at it!

4th LACKEY: Keep shinin' and shut yer trap! Shit!

HUFNAGEL: (*to the* PROFESSOR *in order to keep up appearances in the presence of the* LACKEYS) How many stools does Lord Blotton actually own now?

PROFESSOR: Let's see, unless I'm mistaken, Lord Blotton now owns fourteen stools altogether.

2nd LACKEY: Hey, take a look at how that foot's wigglin' around!

1st LACKEY: Wigglin' around?

2nd LACKEY: Yes, like it was tryin' to nudge me or somethin'. Have a look!

3rd LACKEY: It's movin' around sort of funnylike . . . like it was tryin' to nudge somebody, huh?

LACKEYS: Eeee! What's the matter with that foot?

PROFESSOR: However, in view of the fact that he has already offered two stools to Lady Astley, Lord Blotton may now only have twelve stools, p-p-puuu. . . .

HUFNAGEL: So our dear Lord Blotton may have no more than twelve stools?

PROFESSOR: . . .uuuuke!

2nd LACKEY: Hey, fellas! I recognize it! That's Joey's foot! That's Joey!

1st LACKEY: Joey?

LACKEYS: Joey! That's our Joey!

HUFNAGEL: And I thought that Lord Blotton had at least sixteen stools.

PROFESSOR: He would have had sixteen if two hadn't been given to Marquis de Peet and two, as I said, to Lady Astley. And I'm pu. . . I'm pu. . . I'm pu. . . right. I'm pu. . . left. I'm puking and puking. Puke. I feel sick. Nausea. Vomit. Puke. Puke. Breadthwise and lengthwise. Depthwise and crosswise. Puke. Puke. What nausea. I feel faint, sick, nauseous, queasy, I'm throwing up, I'm heaving, I'm vomiting up my vomit in a radical, absolute, universal, cosmic, physical, metaphysical, omnipotent, all-encompassing and categorical vomit, vomit, vomit, vomit!

HUFNAGEL: A kick! A kick! A kick! Just a second, as soon as I get my foot loose. (*To the* LACKEYS) Get away! (*The* LACKEYS *withdraw;* HUFNAGEL *kicks the* PROFESSOR) There!

PROFESSOR: Oh! God bless you! That is, bless you, but not God! There is no God. There's only a situation. I'm in a situation. I must choose. I choose revolution. I feel better now. The revolution!

HUFNAGEL:
Yes, the revolution!
The revolution of the proletariat!

They take off their masks.

PROFESSOR: Yes, the revolution, but don't give me away, Joseph!
I'm responsible. I'm the one who got you in here, Joseph.

HUFNAGEL: Getting cold feet, Professor? That only proves that
you have no confidence in revolutionary action. Confidence in
revolutionary action is an indispensable condition for the
success of that revolutionary action. Revolutionary action is
divided into stages and develops according to a plan. The first
stage: infiltration into the very heart of the aristocracy and the
bourgeoisie. That's already been carried out.

PROFESSOR: Carried out, carried out, but when it comes out that
Joseph, a former valet of the prince who was dismissed six
years ago for insubordination . . . and later sentenced to five
years in prison for political agitation. . . .

HUFNAGEL: Afraid?

PROFESSOR: Well, all the same. . . .

HUFNAGEL: I would remind you of Paragraph 137B of our
Revolutionary Theory.

PROFESSOR: 137B? Oh yes, of course. According to that paragraph my mentality is the mentality of a bourgeois, in other
words, a mentality completely warped by class exploitation, so
much so that everything I think and feel is perverted, sick, evil,
false, erroneous. . . . Consequently, my present anxiety is also
warped, utterly corrupt at the root and I should rid myself of it,
expel it, dismiss it, disgorge it, eject it. . . . Puuu. . . . Puuu. . . .
Puke! Puke!

HUFNAGEL: A kick! (*He kicks him*)

PROFESSOR: Thanks! It's better now! Thanks! (*He rubs the seat
of his pants*) Oh, how I hate myself!

HUFNAGEL: (*sullenly*) You hate yourself, bourgeois?

PROFESSOR:

    I hate myself
    But I likewise hate this hatred of mine
    Because it's mine! A product of me!
    Who is it that hates?
    It is *I* who hate! I! I, a bourgeois!
    I am the pathological product of a sick system
    I, a morbid tumour, I, an ulcer, I, a disease
    Consumed to the core by a social sin
    And so I hate myself . . . but I also hate
    This hatred of mine . . . and again I hate
    The hatred of my hatred which also hates
    My hatred . . . and I'm puking, puking, puking!

HUFNAGEL: You rotten scum. . . .

PROFESSOR: If I could only . . . puke up myself. . . .

HUFNAGEL:

    Console yourself, worm, we will crush you.
    The revolution will liquidate you.

PROFESSOR: I know. Thanks. Oh yes!

HUFNAGEL: The revolutionary action is in progress. The first stage, as I said, is to infiltrate into the very heart of the bourgeoisie. The second stage: to establish contact with the exploited class. That's in progress. (*More softly*) They recognized my foot! They know who I am! The third stage of revolutionary action: to incite all the destructive elements to bring about a social upheaval. In progress. You have to admit that my idea with those sacks wasn't bad! Sacks create an atmosphere of conspiracy and anarchy, and will facilitate the liberation of those hidden poisons inherent in the present structural phase of the historical process. Just you wait and see!

PROFESSOR: Puke (HUFNAGEL *kicks him*) Oh, thanks!

HUFNAGEL: Intellectuals can be divided into two groups: those who have never got a kick in the backside, and those who have got a kick in the backside. The latter are more sensible.

PROFESSOR: Frankly, Joseph, your revolutionary action strikes

me as being utterly absurd, idiotic and irresponsible. And as for
you, Joseph, I consider you to be as narrow-minded as you are
insane, a simpleton, an ignoramus, a semi-educated moron and
a numbskull. So you see, Joseph, I have every reason to keep
clear of these harebrained enterprises. . . . But who is it that
reasons this way? Me. And who am I? I am a man thoroughly
warped by class exploitation. I am a bourgeois. A class enemy.
Ergo, my opinions about Joseph and about revolutionary action
have to be disgorged by me along with myself, along with
myself, along with myself. Puke! Puke! Puke!

They enter the ballroom. Silence.

ALBERTINE: *(in her sleep)* Nu. . . nuuuuuude. . . .

Enter FIOR.

FIOR:
It's quiet.
Calm.
To understand. . . .
To comprehend. . . .
To be aware. . . .
It's quiet. Calm. Nothing is moving.

ALBERTINE: *(in her sleep)* Nuuu. . . nuuuuuude. . . .

FIOR:
What's got into her?

Silence.

Nothing is moving, everything is rushing
Forward at full tilt. . . .

Silence.

Toward what?

A violent wind; the lights sway to and fro; the windows rattle.

ALBERTINE: *(in her sleep)* Nuuu. . . .

From either side of the stage enter CHARMANT *and* FIRULET *in
top hats and cloaks, each holding a pistol and his* PICKPOCKET
on a leash. Upstage, the witnesses appear.

CHARMANT & FIRULET: Fire!

They shoot, miss each other, change places, bow to each other.

Fire!

They shoot.

FIRULET: I pass!

CHARMANT: I pass!

They throw away their pistols. They approach one another holding their PICKPOCKETS *on leash.*

CHARMANT: Cursed one. . . . I'd like to kill you, kill you, kill you. . . .

FIRULET: Cursed one. . . . I'd like to kill you, kill you, kill you. . . .

CHARMANT: Annihilate you. . . .

FIRULET: Exterminate you. . . .

They stare at one another.

CHARMANT: It was like shooting in a mirror.

FIRULET: It was like shooting in a mirror.

ALBERTINE: (*in her sleep*) Nuuu . . . u . . . u. . . .

CHARMANT & FIRULET: There she goes again!

FIRULET: (*confidentially*) Undress yourself. . . .

CHARMANT: (*confidentially*) Undress yourself. . . .

FIRULET: (*defiantly*) I'm taking off my pants!

CHARMANT: (*defiantly*) I'm taking off my pants!

FIRULET: I pass!

CHARMANT: I pass!

FIRULET: Helas!

CHARMANT: Helas!

FIRULET: (*confidentially*)
  Your decrepitly emaciated. . . .
  Your anaemically rheumatic. . . .
  Your fastidiously coddled. . . .

CHARMANT: (*confidentially*)
  Your primly pampered. . . .
  Your delicately debilitated. . . .
  Your nastily deformed. . . .

FIRULET: Are you talking to yourself?

CHARMANT: No, to you!

FIRULET: I to you to myself.

CHARMANT: I to myself to you.

FIRULET: I pass!

CHARMANT: I pass!

ALBERTINE: (*in her sleep*) Nude. . . .

CHARMANT & FIRULET: There she goes again!

FIRULET: Oh, how annoying!

CHARMANT: (*feverishly*) . . . she thinks that it was I who . . . that
  it was I who stuck my hand down there. . . .

FIRULET:
  But it wasn't you, count! So stick it down there now!
  And if you've no desire to, then keep a tight rein
  On your pickpocket or he'll fondle her again
  The way he did before!

  The PICKPOCKETS *tug at their leashes.*

CHARMANT:
  Those cursed dogs! They're free to do anything!
  While I must always feel ashamed!

ALBERTINE: (*in her sleep*) Nuuu. . . .

CHARMANT & FIRULET: (*holding back their* PICKPOCKETS)
  There she is again!
  Those cursed dogs!

Music. Out of the ballroom come the PRINCE, *the* PRINCESS, *the*
PRIEST, FIOR *and the guests in the most fantastic costumes: a*
sultan, an houri, a shepherdess, etc. Behind them the
SACKBEARERS, *i.e. the* BANKER, *the* GENERAL, *the* MARCHION-
ESS, HUFNAGEL *and the* PROFESSOR. ALBERTINE *is standing*
upstage on the platform. Next to her are standing the group of
LACKEYS, CHARMANT *and* FIRULET *with their* PICKPOCKETS *on*
the proscenium. A sort of somnolent quadrille; all twirl about
in a dancing and comatose motion.

ALL: (*piano*)
   Oh, oh, oh, oh, it's the ball after all!
   Oh, oh, oh, oh, 'tis indeed a ball!

PRINCE & PRINCESS:
   O ball of balls, O wondrous ball
   It glitters with the glitter of every hall!
   So come join the fun, let everyone dance
   May the rhythm of the ball lull you in a trance!

ALL: (*louder*)
   So come join the fun, let everyone dance
   May the ball's proud moustache twirl in a trance!

FIOR:
   O ball, O ball! Oh, what a ball!
   Let each his own in secret dream!
   Then will the master from out of these schemes
   The statue of the future to the world reveal!

SACKBEARERS: (*frantically, dancing*)
   Geeaoo papagoo kookoo go
   Eeepatapoo tatasama
   Tanfargoo feeoooo ee bzzzoooo
   Fizz ppp rrr gr gr tootaoot!

HUFNAGEL: And revolution!

PROFESSOR: Puke, puke, puke!

PRIEST: Et fiat voltas tua!

ALL:
   Oh, oh, oh, oh, it's the ball after all!
   Oh, oh, oh, oh, 'tis indeed a ball!

LACKEYS: (*ferociously*) Tear their legs out!

PROFESSOR: Puke, puke, puke!

PRINCE: (*strolling with the* PRINCESS *and greeting the guests*)
   Ah, ah, bonjour, ah, ah, merci!

   Let everyone dance to the melody!
   Once the dance has carried you away
   Don't bother to ask what the orchestra will play!

PRINCESS:
   Oh, enchantée, ah, ah, charmée
   The ball has climbed into a sack! Alas!
   If the ball's in a sack, don't ask, just dance
   Don't bother to ask what's inside the sack!

PRINCE & PRINCESS: Bonne mine à mauvais jeu!

ALL:
   Ho, ho, ho, ho, a ball, a ball!
   Oh, oh, oh, oh, 'tis indeed a ball!

PRIEST: Et fiat voltas tua!

CHARMANT: (*to his* PICKPOCKET)
   Hey, old boy, what's got into you anyway?
   Stop pulling on the leash that way!
   Mais quelles manières! What a disgrace!
   What are you itching for anyway!

FIRULET: (*to his* PICKPOCKET)
   Hey, old boy, what's got into you?
   What is it you keep itching for?
   What are you up to, you devil, you?
   Oh, la, la, quelles manières!

ALL:
   Oh, la, la, quelles manières!

CHARMANT: (*sadly*)
   And she just keeps on sleeping!

FIRULET: (*sadly*)
   And she just keeps on sleeping!

FIOR: (*with astonishment*)
And she just keeps on sleeping. . . .

PRINCE & PRINCESS:
And she just keeps on sleeping. . . .

Quiet.

PRINCESS: (*stopping*) Why is it so quiet?

ALBERTINE: (*in her sleep*) Nuuuuuude. . . . Nuude. . . .

The PICKPOCKETS *begin to thrash about.*

FIOR: (*suddenly alarmed*)
If nudity has invaded the fashion show
What am I to do? What am I to do.

PRINCE: (*in a loud voice*)
Down with nudity! Let's all dance!
Even if you're dancing on a powder keg
That's no reason to fall out of step!

PRINCESS: (*dramatically*) Let everyone dance!

SACKBEARERS: (*frantically*) Bzzz . . . teee . . . toota . . . tooa . . .
eeeeeet!

LACKEYS: (*fiercely*) Tear their legs out!

HUFNAGEL: The revolution!

PROFESSOR: Puke, puke, puke!

CHARMANT: (*sullenly*) And she just keeps on sleeping!

FIRULET: (*sullenly*) And she just keeps on sleeping!

Silence.

PRINCESS: Why this silence?

ALBERTINE: (*in her sleep*) Nuuuuuuude. . . .

PRINCE: Let everyone dance!

Silence. Dance.

ALBERTINE: (*in her sleep*) Nuuuude. . . .

Silence. A somnolent dance.

CHARMANT: (*suddenly*) I pass!

FIRULET: I pass!

CHARMANT: (*dramatically*) I pass! I can't anymore! I'm unleashing mine! I'm letting mine loose!

FIRULET:
You're what, count?

CHARMANT:
I'm letting him loose! Let him run where he pleases!
Let him have his fling!
If I'm unable to, then let him at least. . . .
I'm letting him loose!

FIRULET:
Stop! If you, count,
Unleash yours, I'll unleash mine. . . .
By God, I'll unleash him. . . .

CHARMANT: Go ahead, unleash him! I don't care!

They unleash the PICKPOCKETS *who disappear among the guests.*

CHARMANT: Let them run! Let them have their fun!

FIRULET: Let them poke their fingers into everything!

CHARMANT: Let them paw whomever they like!

FIRULET: Let them play tricks to their hearts' content!

CHARMANT & FIRULET: We pass! We pass! We pass!

PRINCE & PRINCESS: Let's dance, let's dance, let's dance!

PRINCESS: (*turning in a dancing motion*)
Oh, enchantée, ah, ah, charmée
Bonjour, bonjour! Merci, merci!
Once the dance has carried you away
Don't bother to ask what the orchestra will play!

ALL:
Oh, oh, oh, oh, oh, oh, it's the ball after all!

Oh, oh, oh, oh, oh, 'tis indeed a ball!

SACKBEARERS: (*shrilly*) Toomeefatooeet toopootoo!
Eetooeetookoo!

LACKEYS: (*fiercely*) Tear their legs out!

HUFNAGEL: The revolution!

PROFESSOR: Puke, puke, puke!

PRIEST: Et fiat voltas tua!

PRINCE:
Bonjour, bonjour! Merci, merci!
Let everyone dance to the melody!
Let's dance and dance and never let up!
With never a pause, let's dance, come on!

PRINCESS:
On, enchantée, ah, ah, charmée
By God, let's dance!

All turn about in a somnolent dance. Only ALBERTINE *who is asleep on the platform with the group of* LACKEYS *on one side and* CHARMANT *and* FIRULET *on the other, remain frozen in an attitude of expectation. A sudden squeal from one of the* LADIES.

LADY: Eeeeeeee!

PRINCE & PRINCESS: (*dancing*) Tra-la-la!

ANOTHER LADY: Eeeeeeee!

PRINCE: Tra-la-la!

VOICES: (*squealing*) Eeeeeee! I'm ticklish!

One of the PICKPOCKETS *is seen slipping away with a stolen purse.*

SACKBEARERS: Oooeettttttteeboobooaaaaaapeet!

PRINCESS: What is it now?!

The dance is breathing its last; the other PICKPOCKET *slips away with some stolen jewellery.*

ONE OF THE GENTLEMEN: (*squealing*) Eeeee! Whose hand is *that*?!

LADIES: Dear, dear! I'm ticklish!

GENTLEMEN: You're tickling me, madam!

LADY: That's you!

SACKBEARERS: Tooootampaoomoobootoopataeeteet!

VOICES: I protest!. . . What manners!. . . Oh! A hand!. . . I beg your pardon, sir?!. . . I beg your pardon, madam?!. . . Oh, my back!. . . Ay, ay, ay, my leg!. . . Oh, my bust!

The light has likewise gone berserk, dimming and then lighting up again. The PICKPOCKETS *slip in and out with their plunder. General mayhem.*

PRINCE & PRINCESS: Back to the dance! Let's all dance!

VOICES: (*screaming*) Why are you tickling me, sir?!. . . I beg your pardon, madam?!. . . What's your hand doing down there?!. . . Help! I'm being pawed!. . . Hee, hee, hee, hee! Get away! That tickles!. . . Oh, dear!. . . Ay, ay, ay!. . . Oh, oh!. . . Police! Poliiiice!

SACKBEARERS: Toopaltamamtamoob!

CHARMANT: (*shouting*) I pass!

FIRULET: (*shouting*) I pass!

With one leap HUFNAGEL *mounts the* PROFESSOR *and sitting on him horseback-style — both in sacks and masks — he charges toward the crowd of guests at the head of the Squadron of* LACKEYS.

HUFNAGEL: Hey, at a gallop!

SACKBEARERS: Tootootoo!

The light dims. Silence.

A VOICE: (*shouting in the darkness*) The revolution!

LACKEYS: Tear their legs out! Enough of this shoe-polishing!

SACKBEARERS: Tooptooptoop! Ah pooeet!

Darkness. Silence.

FIOR: (*off to the side, turning on a flashlight*) Lucky thing I
always carry my flashlight with me. Lucky thing I always carry
my flashlight with me. This needs looking into . . . a little
investigating . . . to see what's what. . . .

Slowly he illuminates the motionless guests, the Squadron of
LACKEYS *and* HUFNAGEL *astride the* PROFESSOR. *The costumes
of the guests are in a frightful state, partly tattered, with arms
and bosoms exposed and hands frozen in the act of pinching
and tickling. . . .* FIOR's *flashlight finds both* PICKPOCKETS
frozen in the act of stealing. . . . The light is then directed at
ALBERTINE.

FIOR: And she just keeps on sleeping. . . .

He illuminates CHARMANT *and* FIRULET, *both aghast with
horror. He illuminates the* PRINCE *and* PRINCESS *with their
tattered costumes. He illuminates* HUFNAGEL *who is now
without his mask and sack: a bloody, gruesome face filled with
hatred.*

Aha, Count Hufnagel. . . . He's thrown off his mask. . . . But
what kind of new fashion is that?

He illuminates the GENERAL *whose mask has been half torn
away and whose sack has been rent. The* GENERAL *is dressed in
the uniform of a Nazi officer, with a monocle and a revolver. . . .*

Ah! That was our general who was in that sack! But what sort
of fashion has he devised for himself?

He illuminates the MARCHIONESS, *now minus mask and sack;
she is disguised as an overseer in a German concentration
camp, with whip and handcuffs, etc.*

The marchioness. . . But what kind of fashion is this they've
dreamt up?. . . Please!

He illuminates the BANKER *who is without his mask; but he has
another mask on his face now, a gas mask with a gigantic
nozzle; in his hand is a bomb.*

It looks as if the Banker has. . . .

A violent thunderclap. Wind. Darkness.

CHARMANT: (*yelling*) I pass!

FIRULET: (*yelling*) I pass!

Curtain.

ACT THREE

The ruins of the Himalay Castle. The same hall, but in ruins. The walls have collapsed, only a few pieces of furniture remain; a table covered with a tapestry, a floor lamp, armchairs. . . . Upstage, rubble. A furious wind, a storm. Through breaches in the wall is seen a mysterious sky, flames, flashes of light, a red glow. . . . FIOR *in a frock coat.*

FIOR: (*fighting against the wind*) Is anybody here?

PRINCE: (*with a big lampshade on his head concealing his face; he makes believe that he is a lamp*) A lamp.

FIOR: (*springing back*) Who?

THE PRINCE-LAMP: A lamp.

FIOR: It's the Prince!

THE PRINCE-LAMP: Shh. . . . Shh. . . . For goodness' sake! Be careful!

FIOR: (*shouting in the wind*) What a wind!

THE PRINCE-LAMP: It's the wind of history!

The wind howls.

FIOR: Where is everybody?

THE PRINCE-LAMP: Scattered . . . lost. . . .

FIOR: Was it an earthquake?

THE PRINCE-LAMP: There's no telling! Something happened all right, but there's no telling what!

FIOR: And the Princess?

THE PRINCE-LAMP: She's right here. Don't you recognize her? She's pretending to be a table.

FIOR: (*jumping away from the table which is none other than the* PRINCESS *on all fours, covered with a tapestry*) Ah!

THE PRINCE-LAMP: Shh. . . . It's safer.

Galloping on top of the PROFESSOR, HUFNAGEL *rumbles across the stage at the head of the Squadron of* LACKEYS *who are triumphantly waving various articles of clothing belonging to their masters.*

HUFNAGEL: (*whipping the Professor*) Hey, gallop, gallop!

LACKEYS: Tear their legs out!

They race by.

FIOR: A revolution?

THE PRINCE-LAMP: Yes, a revolution. . . .

Enter a BEGGAR *singing a beggar's song.*

BEGGAR:
Oh, relief for the poor. . . .
Oh, mercy milords. . . .
Oh, alms for the poor!
Oh, the green, green birch. . . .
Oh, the green, green beech. . . .

FIOR: Who are you?

BEGGAR:
Oh, the green, green birch. . . .
Oh, the green, green beech. . . .

FIOR: Who are you anyway?

BEGGAR: (*suddenly*) The stools of Lord Blotton!

He runs out.

FIOR:
What has happened?
Something has happened. . . . But what?

THE PRINCE-LAMP:
>I don't know myself . . . something to do with nudity. . . .
>As though. . . . I don't know. . . . Then came the laughter and
>   squeals. . . .
>People started squealing as if they were being tickled
>Something was tickling me too . . . in my back . . . and along
>my   sides.
>Then my watch disappeared. People began pushing
>Giggling, twittering, shrieking, tee-heeing. . . .
>All hell broke loose. And then the lackeys
>The lackeys started rushing at their masters. . . .
>
>You know, it was just like what you read in the newspapers:
>'subversive elements have taken advantage of the situation. . . .'

FIOR: Yes, yes . . . that's exactly what happened. . . . But now
what?

THE PRINCE-LAMP: (*ambiguously*) The vermin.

The Squadron of LACKEYS *storms in again with* HUFNAGEL
mounted on the PROFESSOR.

LACKEYS: Tear their legs out!

They race by.

FIOR: And what was that?

THE PRINCE-LAMP: I don't know.

FIOR: Why are they racing like that?

THE PRINCE-LAMP: To be racing.

Wind.

FIOR:
>Forms bizarre, forms berserk
>Uncanny, unknown, opaque, obscure. . . .
>No, I don't understand, I don't comprehend. . . .
>Oh, Fior! Oh, poor, poor Fior!

PRINCE & PRINCESS: Poor Master Fior!

The PRIEST *emerges from a pile of debris. His cassock is pinned*

up in such a way that it looks like a blouse and skirt. On his
head is a large woman's hat; in his hand an umbrella.

FIOR: Woman in black, who are you?

THE PRIEST-WOMAN: Master!

FIOR: Ah, that's a cassock!

THE PRIEST-WOMAN: Et fiat voluntas tua. . . .

FIOR: Reverend Father, what fate have you suffered?

THE PRIEST-WOMAN:
   Impossible to say.
   Words cannot express it. Please do not ask
   About the roads that I have travelled. Please do not ask
   About anything at all. I must hide myself.
   Forgive me, but I must hide myself. And you, sir,
   I'd advise to do the same.

FIOR: Am I going to turn into a woman, a lamp or a table? No! I
   am Fior!

PRIEST: Fior!

PRINCESS: Fior!

   HUFNAGEL *comes rushing in at the head of the* LACKEYS.
   Thunder. Darkness.

LACKEYS: Tear their shanks out!

FIOR: You monster! Stop!

HUFNAGEL-RIDER: I can't! I'm the gallop!

FIOR: (*pointing to the* PROFESSOR) And that horse?

THE PROFESSOR-HORSE: Puke!

FIOR: Whom are you chasing?

HUFNAGEL-RIDER: Those who escape!

FIOR: Your face is all bloody, but still I recognize you. You're
   Hufnagel, the count!

HUFNAGEL-RIDER:
   No! I'm an idea!
   Out of the way!

FIOR:
   Professor!
   Is that you, professor?

The PROFESSOR, *on all fours, saddled, with a bridle in his mouth, prances and snorts.*

THE PROFESSOR-HORSE:
   Oh yes, oh yes, thanks!
   Puke! Puke!

LACKEYS:
   Tear their legs out!

HUFNAGEL-RIDER:
   Forward!

They rush out.

FIOR:
   Oh, what a chase!
   Oh, what a race!

Running in the same direction, the GENERAL, *the* BANKER *and the* MARCHIONESS *come storming in, dressed in the same costumes worn at the end of Act Two.*

FIOR:
   Stop! Whom are you chasing?
   And from whom are you fleeing?

GENERAL, BANKER, MARCHIONESS: Goolootoobooloo!

FIOR:
   Marchioness! So It's you then, it's you!
   The Banker! It's him all right and nobody else!
   Our dear friend, the Banker! And you, General!
   Have you all forgotten how to speak?!

THE PRINCE-LAMP:
> When human affairs
> Can't be squeezed into words
> Human speech explodes. . . .

THE PRIEST-WOMAN: Who are these people anyway? Does anybody know them?

THE PRINCESS-TABLE: Ugh! Ugh! Riff-raff. . . .

She slowly raises herself up, still draped with the tapestry.

FIOR:
> Friends!
> Be yourselves again! Get rid of those disguises!
> Enough of these games, it's much too painful!

THE PRINCE-LAMP: The point is they *can't* be themselves any more.

THE PRIEST-WOMAN: There's no possible way.

THE PRINCESS-TABLE: Be ourselves again? How, I'd like to know?

FIOR: What's to be done then?

PRINCE, PRINCESS, PRIEST:
> Forward!
> Always forward! At breakneck speed!
> Forward, forward! In full career!

HUFNAGEL *comes charging in with the* LACKEYS.

HUFNAGEL-RIDER: Gallop, gallop!

He notices the GENERAL, *the* BANKER *and the* MARCHIONESS.

It's them! Catch them!

BANKER, GENERAL, MARCHIONESS: Tooeefeetoooooootatooahh!

The LACKEYS *seize them.*

FIOR: (*to* HUFNAGEL) What are you planning on doing?

HUFNAGEL-RIDER: What? I don't know. But in any case I'll tear out their legs!

To the LACKEYS.

Tear 'em out!

FIOR: Oh, for the love of God!

THE PRINCESS-TABLE: (*to herself*) Well I never. . . .

THE PRIEST-WOMAN: Here goes. . . .

THE PRINCE-LAMP: Ah, well. . . .

HUFNAGEL-RIDER: (*at first with difficulty, then with greater ease*)
Tear out. . . .
Tear out their. . . .
Tear out their legs!
First the right one
Then the left one!

LACKEYS: Enough of this shoe-polishing! Come on! Let's go!

HUFNAGEL-RIDER:
Hey, let's gallop, gallop, gallop!
Let's gallop and gallop, horray, horrah!

THE PROFESSOR-HORSE: And puke, and puke, and puke!

FIOR: Stop! Not without a trial!

THE PRINCESS-TABLE: A trial! Well, I like that!

THE PRINCE-LAMP: A trial?

THE PROFESSOR-HORSE: Puke!

THE PRIEST-WOMAN: What a wind!

FIOR: I must not be seeing right, I don't get it, I don't understand, I don't know, but what I do know is that a trial is
necessary, that without a trial one can't, one shouldn't. . . . How
is it possible . . . without a trial?. . . No, without a trial it's
impossible!

THE PRIEST-WOMAN: What a wind!

THE PRINCE-LAMP: He's clinging to that trial of his like a drunkard to a fence. . . .

THE PRIEST-WOMAN: And there's a wind blowing too. . . .

THE PRINCE-LAMP: (*loudly*) Why a trial? Tear the legs off those
   traitors, those bourgeois, those fascists!

THE PRINCESS-TABLE: Those Nazis!

FIOR:

   Fascists? Nazis? What are those?
   I don't know a thing.

   That goes beyond me, that bowls me over, that overwhelms me,
   yes, I'm overwhelmed, overbowled, overpowered, overawed, I
   don't know anything, I don't know anything, but I do know that
   without a trial, no, no, no, without a trial. . . . An investigation!
   Let there be an investigation!

HUFNAGEL-RIDER:

   It's storming and he demands a trial!
   Lightning is crashing and he would like a trial!
   An investigation when nothing's to be seen
   And night reigns supreme. . . .

   The stage becomes suddenly dark; a storm.

THE PRIEST-WOMAN: Well I. . . . Hold on tight everybody. . . .

THE PRINCE-LAMP: Oof! Oof!

THE PRINCESS-TABLE: Dear, dear!

FIOR: (*reeling against the wind*) A trial! A trial! I demand a trial!

   Thunderclap; the storm subsides; it clears up a little.

HUFNAGEL-RIDER: You pettifogger! All right, you shall have
   your trial. I'll sit down over here. Let the accused, those fas-
   cist-nazi dogs, line up over here! I appoint my horse as
   prosecutor, and you as counsel for the defence. Now on with it!
   We'll settle this at a gallop! The wind is too strong and it may
   start pouring any minute now. So come on! Let's gallop! (*To
   the* PROFESSOR) And you, my horse, begin your indictment!

THE PROFESSOR-HORSE: Puke, I'm puking, puke, puke, puke,
   puke, I'm puking, puke, I'm puking! Puke, puke, puke, puke!

HUFNAGEL-RIDER: Dogs!

THE PRINCE-LAMP: Knaves!

THE PRINCESS-TABLE: Thugs!

THE PRIEST-WOMAN: Dogs!

THE PROFESSOR-HORSE: Puke, puke, puke!

HUFNAGEL, PRINCE & PRINCESS, PRIEST: Guilty! Tear out their legs!

A violent wind.

THE PRIEST-WOMAN: How draughty it is! What a wind!

FIOR: Stop! That horse hasn't said anything! Puking is not a language!

HUFNAGEL-RIDER: So it's speeches you want, eh pettifogger? A crime committed against the proletariat for milleniums, a monumental, silent, mute, inarticulate, monstrous, heinous, onerous, oppressive crime that has been going on for hundreds of centuries, from one generation to another, in silence, without a word, hushed up, never articulated. . . . And with all that silence you would like someone to make a little speech? Enough of this idle chatter! Fascists, bourgeois, dogs! Tear out their legs! Hurry! The storm is here!

LACKEYS: Tear 'em out!

FIOR: I demand they be given a hearing!

HUFNAGEL-RIDER: The storm!

FIOR: Stop! Stop!

HUFNAGEL-RIDER: The storm!

FIOR: Oh, give them a hearing!

HUFNAGEL-RIDER: What a stubbornhead! All right. The revolutionary tribunal will hear the accused. What have you got to say in your defence? Come on!

GENERAL, BANKER, MARCHIONESS: (*getting muddled up in long and panicky explanations*) Ooeetpootooammaaaeetrookoo-

leetakoomabooa lee
naarreeiiooloooooiiiiteerffoolohnbgdshoolfe-
eteemnmfrgshklohkiioregvatssdolpvchgooeertalknihhggghbgootoopatag
totootooletmevutoopioygooil.

GENERAL: Gooloogooloogooloogooloo!

PRINCESS: It's just as if he was gargling!

HUFNAGEL-RIDER: Enough! Guilty!

FIOR: (*trying to outshout the wind*)
I protest!
In spite of all that's been said
Something still remains unsaid!

HUFNAGEL-RIDER: Words are like the wind! Prosecutor! What is your verdict?

THE PROFESSOR-HORSE: Puke!

LACKEYS: Their shanks!

FIOR: Stop!

HUGNAGEL-RIDER: The storm!

FIOR: Stop!

HUFNAGEL-RIDER: The storm!

FIOR:
I declare
That I don't understand, neither who, nor whom, nor why,
Nor what for. No, I don't understand! I don't understand!
I don't understand!

HUFNAGEL-RIDER: The storm!

THE PRINCE-LAMP: The storm!

THE PROFESSOR-HORSE: The storm!

FIOR: Oh, horror, horror, horror!

HUFNAGEL-RIDER: Now off with them to horror!

PRINCE & PRINCESS, PRIEST: The storm!

LACKEYS: The storm!

FIOR: (*to* HUFNAGEL) Be a man again! Throw off your mask!

HUFNAGEL, LACKEYS, PRINCE & PRINCESS, PRIEST: The storm!

A gale, thunder, lightning.

FIOR:
Here one mask is tormenting another!
Off with those masks! Be normal people again!

ALL: The storm! The storm!

GENERAL, BANKER, MARCHIONESS: Ooeetookookmakolatatato-obooboolgoolooloogoolool!

FIOR: (*frantically*) Tooeetookoeeeettootoobolitavateeee!

ALL: (*frantically*) Taftatookooeeeeeeteeookalapataloo!

A gale, thunder, darkness. The wind subsides, the weather clears up. Enter CHARMANT *and* FIRULET *in rural attire, each wearing a straw hat and carrying a butterfly net. The painted faces of clowns, blissful and idiotic. Behind them the* PICKPOCKETS, *in black masks, disguised as gravediggers, carrying a black coffin.*

CHARMANT & FIRULET: (*singing*)
Hey, speckled butterfly
How quickly it flits, I'm after it in a flash!
Hey, speckled butterfly
I'm after it in a flash, ho, ho, in a flash!

Oh, little butterfly, you won't get away
With my little net I'll make you my prey!
Oh, little butterfly, quick as you flit
Out of my net you surely won't slip!

FIOR: They're mad!

THE PRINCE-LAMP:
There is no dearth of madmen today
On the world's great highways and byways. . . .

THE PRIEST-WOMAN:
On the world's vast highways

There's no dearth of the insane. . . .

CHARMANT: (*to* FIRULET)
   Have a look! Isn't that the one
   Who used to be called Fior?

FIRULET: It would seem so. . . .

CHARMANT: (*to* FIOR)
   If I am seeing the remnants of Fior, then Fior is seeing
   The remnants of a count and those of a baron. . . .

FIOR: I used to be Fior. . . .

CHARMANT: I used to be Charmant.

FIRULET: I used to be Firulet . . . once upon a time. . . .

THE PRINCE-LAMP: I used to be called a prince once. . . .

THE PRINCESS-TABLE: And I a princess. . . .

HUFNAGEL-RIDER:
   I was once a lackey until I become
   Hufnagel, a count and a rider. . . .

THE PRIEST-WOMAN: And I was once a priest. . . .

GENERAL: And I a general. . . .

BANKER: And I a banker. . . .

MARCHIONESS: And I a marchioness. . . .

ALL: (*except the* LACKEYS) We used to be, we used to be, we
   used to be, ex, ex, ex.

   Gravely.

   It was, it was. . . .

FIOR:
   Please explain to me, count, tell me, baron
   What's the meaning of that coffin?

CHARMANT: It's a camouflage.

FIRULET: A precautionary measure.

CHARMANT: You see, master, if anyone should stop us, we've
gone crazy, we're walking around with this coffin, we're
lunatics and that's that! But about this coffin. . . .That's an old
and strange story by now. . . . You'd have to go back to that
ball, remember, when heaven knows why, helas, I unleashed
that pickpocket of mine. . . . Helas! It would have been better if
I had never unleashed him, that was the start of all our troubles. . . . But that damned Albertine kept going on about nudity,
nudity, nudity, nudity, nudity, nudity, nudity . . . and I was so
upset on account of that nudity, nudity, nudity, nudity, nudity,
nudity, nudity, nudity, nuu. . . .

FIRULET: I pass!

CHARMANT: I pass! We let those pickpockets loose, Firulet and I,
so they could play a little mischief, raise a little hell. . . .
Because, you see, when you're unable to yourself, then you get
an urge to let such a scamp at least. . . . Laissons! But then!
What a nightmare! Remember, baron?

FIRULET: I remember. . . .

CHARMANT:
They disappear, melt into the crowd
And with their notoriously thievish hands
Their brazenly greedy hands
They're into everything pell mell. . . . Handbags
And necklaces, pockets and purses,
Watches and bracelets. . . . Their paws
They poke into the throng of guests
Through silk and velvet, uniforms and dickeys
Their bodies they tweak, they fondle and tickle
Handle and manhandle till squeals are heard
Shrieks of lust and hysterical laughter. . . .
None of the guests knows who's pawing whom
Their seams all burst, their bosoms flop out
And pants, panties, everything falls apart. . . .

THE PRINCE-LAMP: Yes, I remember. . . . Then my lackeys started
pouncing on my guests. . . .

FIRULET: And we pounced on Albertine!

CHARMANT: But she wasn't there any more!

FIRULET: No, she was gone!

CHARMANT: All we found were the scattered remains of her
wardrobe, including her unmentionables. . . .

FIRULET: Yes, including her unmentionables.

CHARMANT: What a blow!

FIRULET: What a shock! Where could Albertine have been?!

CHARMANT: And the pickpockets were likewise gone. They
vanished like a stone in the water.

Oh, Fior!
Oh, master! What could have happened to her?
Why, it's clear! Those vile dogs! Those dastardly thieves!
Those pickpockets pounced on her, stripped her, raped her
Stole her away from us . . . then took to their heels!

FIRULET: They murdered her!

FIOR: And where is the corpse?

CHARMANT:

There is none! The corpse of her nudity has disappeared!
But for us she's dead! Murdered!
That is why we procured this coffin
And hired these two gravediggers here. . . .

FIRULET:

And on the world's vast highways
We go now in search
Of Albertine's naked body!

CHARMANT: Of Albertine's naked body!

CHARMANT & FIRULET: (*singing*)
Oh, little butterfly, you won't get away
With my little net I'll make you my prey!
Oh, little butterfly, quick as you flit
Out of my net you surely won't slip!

FIRULET: And when we find her, naked, raped and murdered,
we'll conduct a funeral!

FIOR: Excuse me, excuse me, but I don't quite understand, I'm
somewhat at a loss in the haze and the maze of these odd
transformations, transfigurations, transpositions and transmuta-
tions in today's fashion, a fashion, a fashion. . . . A fashion on
the world's devious paths. . . . Oh, what a painful masquerade!
(*pensively*) What's the meaning of that coffin?

THE PRINCE-LAMP: (*approaching*)
O coffin! You appeared just in time!
Hail, O coffin! Allow me to place
My possessions and grandeur in you
My honours and splendours! And all my defeats!

THE PRINCESS-TABLE: (*approaching*)
In this coffin I place my diadems
My pearls and sapphires, my emeralds and diamonds
And all my sighs!

THE PRIEST-WOMAN:
In this coffin I place my God
Go now, the mass is ended!

THE PROFESSOR-HORSE:
Wait!
Just a moment! Don't take away this coffin without me!
Myself I place in it! Puke! Now I no longer am!
Oh, good riddance! At last I am dead!

GENERAL:
Excuse me!
But this coffin is for us! It's meant for us!
For us, the adjudged, the forever condemned!
I place in you, O coffin, the secret
The loathsome, sickening, inscrutable secret
Of that which cannot be expressed!

GENERAL, BANKER,
   MARCHIONESS: Ooeettooeeeetooootootoooeeeeee!

THE PRINCE-LAMP: Woe!

THE PRINCESS-TABLE: Woe, oh woe!

HUFNAGEL-RIDER:
> Hold on! Stop!
> If all have placed their deaths in this coffin
> Then I would ask for a little space too
> Coffin, receive all my hopes, my trials and victories
> The eternal suffering of the proletariat
> The eternal suffering of the proletariat
> And my eternal gallop!

PRINCE & PRINCESS, PROFESSOR, PRIEST:
> Woe, oh woe, oh woe!

CHARMANT & FIRULET:
> Woe, oh woe!

LACKEYS:
> Woe, oh woe, oh woe!

FIOR:
> O bulging coffin, O mournful funeral
> Oh woe, oh woe, oh woe!

ALL:
> Woe! Oh woe!

FIOR *steps forward.*

FIOR:
> Out of the way!
> Step back from that coffin! Let the master approach!
> Let *me* go up to it, I, Master Fior!

ALL:
> O Fior, O Fior, O Fior, O Fior!

FIOR:
> Friends!
> I, Fior, I, the master, I, creator of the mode
> I, the great dictator of fashion and sculptor
> Of the style in vogue. . . .

He approaches the coffin.

> Pass!

CHARMANT:
Pass!

FIRULET:
Pass!

FIOR:
I curse man's clothing, I curse the masks.
Those bloodstained masks that eat into our bodies
I curse the cut of trousers and blouses
They've eaten too far into our flesh!

ALL:
A curse!

FIOR:
I, Fior
I, the master of men's and women's fashion,
I place in this coffin that sacred —
But forever defiled by clothing —
Nudity of man!

ALL:
O sacred nudity, sleep!

FIOR:
O sacred human nudity, sleep forever!
We shall never come to know you. . . .

CHARMANT:
Trousers!

FIRULET:
Jackets!

BANKER:
Stockings!

GENERAL:
Panties!

PRINCESS:
Scarves!

PRINCE:
Cane!

PRIEST:
  Neckties!

MARCHIONESS:
  Petticoats!

HUFNAGEL:
  Boots!

ALL: (*except* FIOR) Puttees, frock coats, shoes, décolletés, shoe-
  laces, frou-frou, mew-mew, déshabillé, smoking jackets, spats,
  et cetera, et cetera, et cetera, et cetera, et cetera. . . .

FIOR:
  O nudity, sacred but unattainable
  Sleep forever!

  He makes a gesture as though he were placing it in the coffin.

VOICE OF ALBERTINE: (*from inside the coffin*) Nuuuuude. . . .

ALL: (*shouting*) What was that?

  Silence.

VOICE OF ALBERTINE:
  Nuuuude. . . .

CHARMANT:
  It's her!

FIRULET:
  It's her!

FIOR:
  Quiet!

  Silence.

VOICE OF ALBERTINE:
  Nuuude. . . .

CHARMANT: (*quickly*)
  It's her!

FIRULET: (*quickly*)
  She's here somewhere!

CHARMANT:
   She's dreaming about my nudity!

FIRULET:
   It's her!

CHARMANT:
   She's here somewhere.

FIRULET:
   She's dreaming about my nudity!

   The lid of the coffin rises and the bare arm of ALBERTINE *appears.*

ALL:
   It's her!

FIOR:
   O, salvation!
   O hail, nudity, eternally youthful!

   ALBERTINE *slowly emerges from the coffin, naked.*

FIOR:
   O hail, ordinary one! O hail, immortal one!

ALL:
   O nudity eternally youthful, hail!

   Apotheosis.

CHARMANT: (*suddenly leaping forward*)
   Pardon!
   Who stuck you in there?
   Who hid you in there?

ALBERTINE: (*pointing to the* GRAVEDIGGERS) They did!

The GRAVEDIGGERS *throw off their masks, revealing the laughing faces of the* PICKPOCKETS.

FIRULET: It's them!

CHARMANT: It's the pickpockets!

BOTH: It's those dogs!

   The remainder of the scene should be sung.

PICKPOCKETS: (*singing*)
  It's us!
  It's us!
  It's us!

ALBERTINE: (*dancing*) I am Albertine!

PICKPOCKETS: (*dancing*) A peach of a thing! A peach of a thing!

ALBERTINE:
  These are my thighs, my hands and feet
  These are my ears and these my teeth
  And these, oh, these are my breasts so petite!

PICKPOCKETS: Those are her thighs and breasts so petite!

ALBERTINE: I am Albertine!

PICKPOCKETS: A peach of a thing! A peach of a thing!

ALBERTINE: Eternally youthful!

PICKPOCKETS: From the grave she rises!

ALBERTINE: On the coffin she dances!

PICKPOCKETS: She wants to have fun!

ALBERTINE & PICKPOCKETS: (*dancing*) Ah, Albertine, a peach of
  a thing, from the grave she rises, eternally youthful, on the
  coffin she dances, she wants to have fun.

  And of love
  And of love
  In the nude
  In the nude
  She dreams without end. . . .

CHARMANT:
  In the nude. . . .

FIRULET:
  In the nude. . . .

CHARMANT & FIRULET:
  Without end, oh, without end, oh, without end,
  She dreams and dreams!

ALL:
>Without end she dreams!
>Without end she dreeeeeeeams!
>Without end she dreeeeeeeeeeeeeams. . .

FIOR, CHARMANT & FIRULET:
>O nudity eternally youthful, hail!
>O youth eternally nude, hail!
>O youthful nudity, nudely youthful
>O nudity of youth, youthfully nude!

FIOR:
>But I don't understand
>I don't get it
>I still don't understand
>How did she get in that coffin there?

ALL: (*except* ALBERTINE *and the* PICKPOCKETS) How did she get in that coffin there?

PICKPOCKETS:
>It was us!
>It was us!
>It was us!

ALBERTINE: It was them, oh yes, it was them, why yes, it was them, it was them, oh yes, it was them, yes, them, oh, them, oh yes, oh yes, it was them, oh yes, it was them!

PICKPOCKETS:
>It was us!
>It was us!
>It was us!

ALL: Why, it was them, it was them, yes, them, yes, them!

PICKPOCKETS:
>It was us!
>It was us!
>It was us!

>*Curtain.*